SWINGS
and
SHADOWS

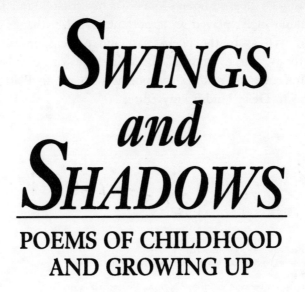

SWINGS
and
SHADOWS

POEMS OF CHILDHOOD
AND GROWING UP

Anne Harvey

Julia MacRae Books
LONDON SYDNEY AUCKLAND JOHANNESBURG

In the making of this anthology many of my friends and family have, perhaps unknowingly, played an important part. My thanks and love go to them, as well as to the poets, past and present, in the book, and especially to my niece Annabel for being the girl on the swing, to Virginia McKenna for reading the poems with me in Platform Performances, and to Delia Huddy, my editor.

Cé /5821   C605746099

First published in the United Kingdom in 1996 by Julia MacRae
Random House, 20 Vauxhall Bridge Road, London SW1V 2SA

Random House Australia (Pty) Limited
20 Alfred Street, Milsons Point, Sydney,
New South Wales 2061, Australia

Random House New Zealand Limited
18 Poland Road, Glenfield, Auckland 10, New Zealand

Random House South Africa (Pty) Limited
PO Box 2263, Rosebank 2121, South Africa

Random House UK Limited Reg. No. 954009
A CIP catalogue record for this book is available from the British Library

ISBN 1-85681-722-9

Papers used by Random House UK Ltd are natural recyclable products made from wood grown in sustainable forests. The manufacturing processes conform to the environmental regulations of the country of origin.

Printed in Great Britain by
Mackays of Chatham PLC, Chatham, Kent

Contents

Introduction   vii

1   TO MAKE A BEGINNING   1

2   IN PLAY IS ALL MY MIND   29

3   THE DARKENING GARDEN   57

4   CHILDHOOD'S FLICKERING SHADOW   81

5   IF I COULD TELL YOU   101

6   TREAD SOFTLY HERE   123

7   SEA-SAND AND SORROW   153

8   PLAY THE TUNE AGAIN   177

9   SPELL OF WORDS   201

10 SHADES OF CHILDHOOD   223

Acknowledgements   241

Index of poets   243

Index of titles and first lines   245

Introduction

My liking for poetry began with the nursery rhymes my mother sang and read to me. I don't know what the baby I was then thought about cows jumping over moons, babies tumbling from tree-tops or fine ladies riding to Banbury Cross with bells on their toes, but I do know that the rhymes, rhythms, nonsense and delight have never left me. Boy Blue, Bo Peep, Contrary Mary and the rest waited in the shadows to return when my own children were small and are back again for my grandchildren. Perhaps it is only now that their real importance, their lasting quality has dawned on me. They are so odd, so unexpected, so funny and so frightening that surely they paved the way for what was to come.

Some of the earliest 'real' poems I heard were way beyond my understanding but this never worried me. When my grandmother declaimed such famous lines as 'The boy stood on the burning deck' or 'My name is Ozymandias, King of Kings' I was quite as enchanted as when our infant teacher confided, 'There are Fairies at the bottom of my garden'... That borderline between the adult and child world is, in poetry, faint and indefinable.

I was lucky right through my wartime schooldays to have teachers who shared and taught poetry in an inspired way. Early on there was much enjoyable learning by heart and speaking aloud, sometimes in chorus. At a later stage came more serious dramatising of favourites like Tennyson's *The Lady of Shalott* and Browning's *The Pied Piper*, in which I can still remember playing the added character of the lame boy's sister. Later still, study and discussion of the First World War Poets, Shakespeare's *Sonnets* or Wordsworth's *Prelude* opened new avenues, revealing the lives of the poets themselves, the discovery of them as real people.

There were always anthologies. My first was *For Your Delight*, and, until quite recently, I thought the editor's name was Ethel M Flower. It was a shock to find it less romantically 'Fowler' especially as the original meaning of 'anthology' was 'a flower gathering' or 'a collection of the flowers of verse'. *For Your Delight* was a stepping-stone with its mixture of short pieces from the classics and more childish verse, still affectionately remembered.

School anthologies were generally dull and unillustrated in my childhood. We did not expect pictures. What artist could bring de la Mare's *Lord of Tartary*, Longfellow's *Hiawatha* or Belloc's *Matilda* to life as vividly as our imaginations?

I don't think I ever said, 'I want to be an anthologist' but at about 13 I began making my own, laboriously copying poems in my best handwriting into exercise books while outside the sun shone, and my parents puzzled over my strange hobby. Then, at Drama School, one of my teachers turned out to be the editor of *An Anthology for Verse Speakers*, E. Guy Pertwee. A delightful eccentric and brilliant teacher of poetry, he had served in the First World War in France alongside the poet, Edward Thomas...a poet whom I had first discovered at school. His poem *Words* had sprung from a page in our *Anthology of Modern Verse* with its contrasts of lightness and depth, its poignant cry: 'Choose me, you English words.' Like many of the War Poets he died in France a year after writing *Words*, but the finest poets live on when their words are re-printed, re-discovered, read over and over again.

The first poem I remember learning 'by heart' out of school was *The Cupboard* by Walter de Mare and immediately it belonged to me. I knew that dark shelf, that key. It was my grandmother with the 'very slippery knee' - hadn't I once glimpsed it when she cautiously raised a flowery skirt to paddle with me in the sea? The sea...always vast and mysterious, but how much more so in John Masefield's *Sea Fever*. Now I was him, longing to return to 'the wind's song and the white sails shaking' - stirring and heart-breaking, this was another key moment in poetry. Unknowingly I was discovering what C.Day Lewis meant when he wrote: 'Poetry is a special way of using words in order to create a special effect upon the reader and to light up the world for him.'

Like Elizabeth Jennings I remember first hearing G.K. Chesterton's *Lepanto* with its beating rhythms and the vivid character of 'Don John laughing in the brave beard curled/ Spurning of his stirrups like the thrones of all the world.'

She recreates this in her poem *A Classroom*, pinpointing that moment when she was

' ...caught up, excited, charged and
changed,
Made ready for the next fine spell
of words,
Locked into language with a golden
key.'

I admit to being a little chastened when a 12-year-old nephew in his essay *'My Most Eccentric Relative'* said, 'Every time my aunt opens her mouth a poem comes out.' Was this a warning to me to keep poetry to myself? As an editor, I couldn't do that; the wish to pass on and share those poems that have somehow lit up the world, charged and changed me, is always there.

Swings and Shadows traces the pattern of my life. The poems I've chosen are not exactly autobiographical but they echo something I remember of childhood and of children, toys and books, theatre, music, dance, people of all ages, the swings and the shadows of a passing time.

Anne Harvey, June 1996

1 · *To make a beginning*

Certainly Adam in Paradise had not more sweet and curious apprehension of the world than I when I was a child... All appeared new and strange at first, inexpressibly rare and delightful and beautiful. I was a little stranger, which at my entrance into the world was saluted and surrounded with innumerable joys... The dust and stones of the street were as precious as gold; the gates were at first the end of the world. The green trees when I saw them first through one of the gates transported and ravished me, their sweetness and unusual beauty made my heart to leap, and almost mad with ecstacy, they were such strange and wonderful things...

> *Thomas Traherne*: CENTURIES OF MEDITATION

Algernon Charles Swinburne... often used to stop my perambulator when he met it on Nurse's Walk at the edge of Wimbledon Common, and pat me on the head and kiss me; he was an inveterate pram-stopper and patter and kisser... Swinburne, by the way, when a very young man, had gone to Walter Savage Landor, then a very old man, and been given the poet's blessing he asked for; and Landor when a child had been patted on the head by Dr Samuel Johnson; and Johnson when a child had been taken to London to be touched by Queen Anne for scrofula, the King's evil; and Queen Anne when a child...

> *Robert Graves*: GOODBYE TO ALL THAT

SPELL OF CREATION

Within the flower there lies a seed,
In the seed there springs a tree,
In the tree there spreads a wood.

In the wood there burns a fire,
And in the fire there melts a stone,
Within the stone a ring of iron.

Within the ring there lies an O,
In the O there looks an eye,
In the eye there swims a sea,

And in the sea reflected sky,
And in the sky there shines the sun,
In the sun a bird of gold.

In the bird there beats a heart,
And from the heart there flows a song,
And in the song there sings a word.

In the word there speaks a world,
A word of joy, a world of grief,
From joy and grief there springs my love.

Oh love, my love, there springs a world,
And on the world there shines a sun,
And in the sun there burns a fire.

In the fire consumes my heart,
And in my heart there beats a bird,
And in the bird there wakes an eye,

Within the eye, earth, sea and sky,
Earth, sky and sea within an O,
Lie like the seeds within the flower.

Kathleen Raine

I REMEMBER, I REMEMBER

I remember, I remember
The house where I was born,
The little window where the sun
Came peeping in at morn;
He never came a wink too soon
Nor brought too long a day;
But now, I often wish the night
Had borne my breath away.

I remember, I remember
The roses, red and white,
The violets, and the lily-cups—
Those flowers made of light!
The lilacs where the robin built,
And where my brother set
The laburnum on his birthday,—
The tree is living yet!

I remember, I remember
Where I was used to swing,
And thought the air must rush as fresh
To swallows on the wing;
My spirit flew in feathers then
That is so heavy now,
The summer pools could hardly cool
The fever on my brow.

I remember, I remember
The fir-trees dark and high;
I used to think their slender tops
Were close against the sky:
It was a childish ignorance,
But now 'tis little joy
To know I'm farther off from Heaven
Than when I was a boy.

Thomas Hood

from AUGURIES OF INNOCENCE

Every night and every morn
Some to misery are born;
Every morn and every night
Some are born to sweet delight;
Some are born to sweet delight,
Some are born to endless night.
Joy and woe are woven fine,
A clothing for the soul divine;
Under every grief and pine
Runs a joy with silken twine.
It is right it should be so;
Man was made for joy and woe;
And when this we rightly know,
Safely through the world we go.

William Blake

TO A CHILD BEFORE BIRTH

This summer is your perfect summer. Never will the skies
So stretched and strident be with blue
As these you do not see; never will the birds surprise
With such light flukes the ferns and fences
As these you do not hear. This year the may
Smells like rum-butter, and day by day
The petals slip from the cups like lover's hands,
Tender and tired and satisfied. This year the haws
Will form as your fingers form, and when in August
The sun first stings your eyes,
The fruit will be red as brick and free to the throstles.
Oh but next year the may
Will have its old smell of plague about it; next year
The songs of the birds be selfish, the skies have rain;
Next year the apples will be tart again.
But do not always grieve
For the unseen summer. Perfection is not the land you leave,
It is the pole you measure from; it gives
Geography to your ways and wanderings.
What is your perfection is another's pain;
And because she in impossible season loves
So in her blood for you the bright bird sings.

Norman Nicholson

� ✻ ✻

THE ETERNAL CHILD

A little child
Enters by a secret door, alone,
Was not, and is,
Carrying his torch aflame.

In pilgrim cloak and hood
Many and many come,
Or is it the one child
Again and again?

What journey do they go,
What quest accomplish, task fulfil?
Whence they cannot say,
Whither we cannot tell,
And yet the way they know.

So many innocents,
Reflections in a torrent thrown:
Can any on these treacherous waters cast
Unmarred, unbroken,
Image the perfect one?

All things seem possible to the new-born;
But each one story tells, one dream
Leaves on the threshold of unbounded night
Where all return
Spent torch and pilgrim shroud.

Kathleen Raine

IN PRAISE OF ISABEL PENNELL

By Saint Mary, my lady,
Your mammy and your daddy
Brought forth a goodly baby!

My maiden Isabell,—
Reflaring[1] rosabell,
The flagrant camamell,

The ruddy rosary,
The sovereign rosemary,
The pretty strawberry,

The columbine, the nepte,[2]
The jelofer[3] well set,
The proper violet,

Ennewèd, your colour
Is like the daisy flower
After the April shower!

Star of the morrow gray,
The blossom on the spray,
The freshest flower of May;

Maidenly demure,
Of womanhood the lure,
Wherefore I make you sure:

It were an heavenly health,
It were an endless wealth,
A life for God himself,

To hear this nightingale,
Among the birdés smale,
Warbling in the vale:—

Dug, dug,
Jug, jug,
Good year and good luck,
With chuk, chuk, chuk, chuk!

John Skelton

¹ Sweet-smelling   ² Cat-mint   ³ Gillyflower

A PROTEST

When I am hungry I must cry.
Do not be misled
By all my conscious airs or by
My head shaped like my father's head,
Or by the expert language of my laughter.
Do not be beguiled
To think I am all essence and hereafter.
I am a six-months child.

E. J. Scovell

from THE SALUTATION

These little limbs,
    These eyes and hands which here I find,
These rosy cheeks wherewith my life begins,
    Where have ye been? Behind
What curtain were ye from me hid so long!
Where was, in what abyss, my speaking tongue?

    When silent I
    So many thousand, thousand years
Beneath the dust did in a chaos lie,
    How could I smiles or tears,
Or lips or hands or eyes or ears perceive?
Welcome ye treasures which I now receive.

    I that so long
    Was nothing from eternity,
Did little think such joys as ear or tongue
    To celebrate or see:
Such sounds to hear, such hands to feel, such feet,
Beneath the skies on such a ground to meet.

    From dust I rise,
    And out of nothing now awake;
These brighter regions which salute mine eyes,
    A gift from God I take.
The earth, the seas, the light, the day, the skies,
The sun and stars are mine, if those I prize.

    A stranger here
    Strange things doth meet, strange glories see;
Strange treasures lodged in this fair world appear
    Strange all and new to me.
But that they mine should be, who nothing was,
That strangest is of all, yet brought to pass.

Thomas Traherne

THE BARDS

My agèd friend, Miss Wilkinson,
   Whose mother was a Lambe,
Saw Wordsworth once, and Coleridge, too,
   One morning in her p'ram'.*

Birdlike the bards stooped over her—
   Like fledgling in a nest;
And Wordsworth said, 'Thou harmless babe!'
   And Coleridge was impressed.

The pretty thing gazed up and smiled,
   And softly murmured, 'Coo!'
William was then aged sixty-four
   And Samuel sixty-two.

* This was a three-wheeled vehicle
   Of iron and of wood;
It had a leather apron,
   But it hadn't any hood.

Walter de la Mare

Rock-a-bye baby
On the treetop,
When the wind blows
The cradle will rock;
When the bough breaks
The cradle will fall,
Down will come baby,
Cradle and all.

HUSH-A-BYE, BABY

All right, dear, I'll not risk bad dreams again
For our small daughter, singing her to sleep
With my sad ballads. Now Sir Patrick Spens
Can stay dry-shod; Queen Jane shall not cry out
For Good King Henry in her agony;
The channering worm shall chide no more; fair Janet
Must leave her true-love to the elf-queen's keeping,
And Arlen's wife will absolutely not
Be pinned right through the heart against the wall.
Henceforth, as you request, I shall confine myself,
Like any normal dad, to nursery rhymes:
Strange egg-shaped characters will smash themselves
Irreparably; ill-housed, harassed mothers
Whip hungry children; babies fall from trees;
Mice shall be maimed; sheep lost; arachnophobes
Fare badly; innocent domestics suffer
Sudden nasectomies, and at the end
We shall dance rosy-faced in a ring and drop dead with the plague.

In either case, outside the small lit bedroom
The glass shall weep with rain, the winds be howling
Their old, uncensorable savageries.
But you are right, of course: we should choose well
What songs we sing, to lull them for a while.

David Sutton

NURSERY RHYME

Hush-a–bye, baby, your milk's in the tin,
Mummy has got you a nice sitter-in;
Hush-a–bye, baby, now don't get a twinge
While Mummy and Daddy are out on the binge.

Anon

VIEW FROM A HIGH CHAIR

Here thump on tray
With mug, and splash
Wet white down there.
The sofa purrs,
The window squeaks.
Bump more with mug
And make voice big
Then she will come,
Sky in the room,
Quiet as a cloud,
Flowers in the sky,
Come down snow-soft
But warm as milk,
Hide all the things
That squint with shine,
That gruff and bite
And want to hurt;
Will swallow us
And taste so sweet
As down we go
To try our feet.

Vernon Scannell

ONE TIMES ONE IS EIGHT

Either old magic or new math
Into our house has beat a path.
How else could Einstein or Diogenes
Explain an exploit of our progeny's?
While at the table with his ilk
A child upsets a glass of milk.
The glass held half a pint when filled,
And half a gallon when it spilled.

Ogden Nash

LEARNING TO GO ALONE

Come, my darling, come away,
Take a pretty walk to-day;
Run along, and never fear,
I'll take care of baby dear:
Up and down with little feet,
That's the way to walk, my sweet.
Now it is so very near,
Soon she'll get to mother dear.
There she comes along at last:
Here's my finger, hold it fast:
Now one pretty little kiss,
After such a walk as this.

Ann & Jane Taylor

TO MY NIECE, A.M. *With a new Pair of Shoes on her first going alone. Written Dec. 22, 1774*

WHEN little girls begin to walk,
Their next attempt should be to talk.
Then why thus, Nancy, why thus long
Do you persist to hold your tongue?
Full sixteen months gone o'er your head,
And not a word by you been said!
Oh! let it never once be told
That silence reigned in girl so old!
But let us hear, by Christmas day,
Your speech at last hath found its way:
In lisping accents sweetly prattle
Of fine new shoes, of doll, and rattle,
And prove to all your friends around
Your sex's province you have found.

Anonymous 'A Female Hand'

HUMAN AFFECTION

Mother, I love you so.
Said the child, I love you more than I know.
She laid her head on her mother's arm,
And the love between them kept them warm.

Stevie Smith

LEARNING TO TALK

See this small one, tiptoe on
The green foothills of the years,
Views a younger world than yours;
When you go down, he'll be the tall one.

Dawn's dew is on his tongue –
No word for what's behind the sky,
Naming all that meets the eye,
Pleased with sunlight over a lawn.

Hear his laughter. He can't contain
The exquisite moment overflowing.
Limbs leaping, woodpecker flying
Are for him and not hereafter.

Tongue trips, recovers, triumphs,
Turning all ways to express
What the forward eye can guess –
That time is his and earth young.

We are growing too like trees
To give the rising wind a voice:
Eagles shall build upon our verse,
Our winged seeds are tomorrow's sowing.

Yes, we learn to speak for all
Whose hearts here are not at home,
All who march to a better time
And breed the world for which they burn.

Though we fall once, though we often,
Though we fall to rise not again,
From our horizon sons begin;
When we go down, they will be tall ones.

C. Day Lewis

A VOICE

The child is slow to speak in words
But makes, as sometimes birds
Or water flowing deep in ground,
A human voice's sound –
Only that theirs could never seem
(The speech of bird or stream
That startles first with likeness, then proves different)
Perfectly human like her speaking, and intelligent.

Foreign voices please the ear
When suddenly we hear
Without the office of the mind
The mere note of our kind.
But hers, that has meaning for none
But lives as sound alone,
Quick, limpid, gentle, seems the soul, distilled from sense,
Of what is human most in man, his tongue's intelligence.

E. J. Scovell

SNOW

In the gloom of whiteness,
In the great silence of snow,
A child was sighing
And bitterly saying: 'Oh,
They have killed a white bird up there on her nest,
The down is fluttering from her breast!'
And still it fell through that dusky brightness
On the child crying for the bird of the snow.

Edward Thomas

TO A SNOWFLAKE

What heart could have thought you?—
Past our devisal
(O filigree petal!)
Fashioned so purely,
Fragilely, surely,
From what Paradisal
Imagineless metal,
Too costly for cost?
Who hammered you, wrought you,
From argentine vapour?—
'God was my shaper.
Passing surmisal,
He hammered, He wrought me,
From curled silver vapour,
To lust of His mind:—
Thou could'st not have thought me!
So purely, so palely,
Tinily, surely,
Mightily, frailly,
Insculped and embossed,
With His hammer of wind,
And His graver of frost.'

Francis Thompson

WHITE SNOW

'White snow', my daughter says, and sees
For the first time the lawn, the trees,
Loaded with this superfluous stuff.
Two words suffice to make facts sure
To her, whose mental furniture
Needs only words to say enough.

Perhaps by next year she'll forget
What she today saw delicate
On every blade of grass and stone;
Yet will she recognize those two
Syllables, and see them through
Eyes which remain when snow has gone?

Season by season, she will learn
The names when seeds sprout, leaves turn,
And every change is commonplace.
She will bear snowfalls in the mind,
Know wretchedness of rain and wind,
With the same eyes in a different face.

My wish for her, who held by me
Looks out now on this mystery
Which she has solved with words of mine,
Is that she may learn to know
That in her words for the white snow
Change and permanence combine—
The snow melted, the trees green,
Sure words for hurts not suffered yet, nor seen.

Anthony Thwaite

CATCH A SNOWFLAKE IF YOU CAN
(In memory of Penny Gee)

Catch a snowflake if you can
see the patterns as they run
hold them melting in your hand
lick your fingers as they numb.

Try to find an icicle
put it in the microwave,
watch it turn into a pool
which the buzzer cannot save.

Nothing is quite what it seems
living is for here and now,
so defrost your frozen dreams
do not wait to question how.

Hold your hands out to the wind
let the rain run down your face,
step in every fairy ring
hide in each enchanted place.

Write your words upon the air
see them curve and rhyme and scan,
make new patterns everywhere
catch a snowflake if you can.

Elizabeth Bewick

PAPA LOVE BABY

My mother was a romantic girl
So she had to marry a man with his hair in curl
Who subsequently became my unrespected papa,
But that was a long time ago now.

What folly it is that daughters are always supposed to be
In love with papa. It wasn't the case with me
I couldn't take to him at all
But he took to me
What a sad fate to befall
A child of three.

I sat upright in my baby carriage
And wished mama hadn't made such a foolish marriage.
I tried to hide it, but it showed in my eyes unfortunately
And a fortnight later papa ran away to sea.

He used to come home on leave
It was always the same
I could not grieve
But I think I was somewhat to blame.

Stevie Smith

Speak when ye're spoken tae,
Dae what ye're bidden,
Come when ye're ca'd,
And ye'll no be chidden.

Scottish Rhyme

THE PURLOINER

As Joe was at play,
Near the cupboard one day,
When he thought no one saw but himself,
How sorry I am,
He ate raspberry jam,
And currants that stood on the shelf.

His mother and John
To the garden had gone,
To gather ripe pears and ripe plums;
What Joe was about
His mother found out,
When she look'd at his fingers and thumbs:

And when they had dined
Said to Joe, 'You will find,
It is better to leave things alone;
These plums and these pears
No naughty boy shares,
Who meddles with fruit not his own.'

Elizabeth Turner

THE CUPBOARD

I know a little cupboard,
With a teeny tiny key,
And there's a jar of Lollipops
   For me, me, me.

It has a little shelf, my dear,
As dark as dark can be,
And there's a dish of Banbury Cakes
   For me, me, me.

I have a small fat grandmamma,
With a very slippery knee,
And she's Keeper of the Cupboard,
   With the key, key, key.

And when I'm very good, my dear,
As good as good can be,
There's Banbury Cakes, and Lollipops
   For me, me, me.

Walter de la Mare

MOGGY AT GRIMMA'S

Fo fum and look at the plunge in Grimma's Arden.
watch the slips! They're a bit properly. Cold my grand.
The gag won't hurt you, he's a wood boggy.
Flat him. Bently! He won't fight, he's only breaking.
A gnashy nose. Brown, Pincer, Brown!
The brass is blush and clamp. The bones are green.

See the clash? Under the breeds?
Goldsplishes and polyglots. Frigs.
All lippery. Mutes under the leavings.
It's all crud at the bottom.
Woeful! Be woeful, brawling, don't want to brumble
you'll get all brat!

Grimma's mouse smells molish and purey
the more's lippery. What's in the hubbub? Names!
Sacks of pards, bluedo and pelicans.
When you are colder, Grimma will play with you,
snappy fumblies, widdley tinks, necks and sadders.
You can go worst because you are longest.

The cock kicks. Grimma grinds up the cock
with her big clay. She grinds and grinds.
The cock goes knick, knock and the time goes bong.

Meet your tickys up. Link up your silk.
It's in your very grown hug with the habits on.
How many habits? Gone. Who. Me! Oh suck
at all those hums! Fetch the weaver,
weep up the hums, all heat and sidy.

Up in the pilchard there are asps
at the blindfold mopples, huzzing in the blowers, hook!
Moreberries under the knotting. This one's all dead,
this one's pipe. Meet it up, bawling and a mother!

Look how star you can be from here! Proud arrows
boating over the sills and alleys, folds and goods,
bright out to the freeside across the way.

Roamtime now. Say butterfly to Grimma, wailing.
Grieve her a miss, grieve her a shrug.
Sun again moon! She bends by the floor and braves.
She braves and braves as Moggy thrives away.

Dorothy Nimmo

I have been a Naughty Girl
I have been a Naughty Girl
The lofty trees their heads do shake
When the wind blows, a noise they make
When they are cut a crash you hear
That fills your very soul with fear
Tis like the thunders loudest roar
You would not like to hear much more
It makes the earth begin to quake
And all its mity pillers shake

from the Journal of Marjory Fleming, aged 7

A CHILD'S GARDEN

Who* was here. Before his cat
Washed and rose. Without his shoes
Who inched outside while someone's hat
Made a noise. Light feet helped. Who's.

Whose are these eggs? Ladybird's.
Hard like crumbs of sleep. She flies
Off to help who find some words
For sounds and things. Who's two puffed eyes

Tug at flowers now for bees
Tucked away. Some try to hide
In pouting fox-gloves' jugs. Who sees
Their fat bear's thighs, though, wedged inside

Scouring honey. Look! Rare stones
In lupin leaves. Who's flapping gown
Shakes them all out. Ow! Who's bones
Aren't awake, make who fall down

Biting earth. Who hears a sound.
Whose are these wet softish hairs
Brushing someone's mouth? Can bound
As quick as you. Whoosh! Peter scares

A thin bird. Zip! Squawk! Its beak
Almost nipped who's fattest worm
Head and tail. Who hears him squeak
Through the grass: who sees him squirm

Down a hole. Who wants to kiss
His frightened worm. Who's coolish knees
Push him up to clematis
He thinks it's called. It makes him sneeze.

Gooseflesh comes. Who's bare toes rake
Up oily slugs. Who wants to hop,
Skip. Who's flopping tassels make
Ants run. Who hears his crispies pop.

George Macbeth

* This small child calls himself Who

THE CHILD AT THE WINDOW

Remember this, when childhood's far away;
The sunlight of a showery first spring day;
You from your house-top window laughing down,
And I, returned with whip-cracks from a ride,
On the great lawn below you, playing the clown.
Time blots our gladness out. Let this with love abide...

The brave March day; and you, not four years old,
Up in your nursery world—all heaven for me.
Remember this—the happiness I hold—
In far off springs I shall not live to see;
The world one map of wastening war unrolled,
And you, unconscious of it, setting my spirit free.

For you must learn, beyond bewildering years,
How little things beloved and held are best.
The windows of the world are blurred with tears,
And troubles come like cloud-banks from the west.
Remember this, some afternoon in spring,
When your own child looks down and makes your sad heart sing.

Siegfried Sassoon

CHILDREN'S SONG

We live in our own world,
A world that is too small
For you to stoop and enter
Even on hands and knees,
The adult subterfuge.
And though you probe and pry
With analytic eye,
And eavesdrop all our talk
With an amused look,
You cannot find the centre
Where we dance, where we play,
Where life is still asleep
Under the closed flower,
Under the smooth shell
Of eggs in the cupped nest
That mock the faded blue
Of your remoter heaven.

R. S. Thomas

2 · *In play is all my mind*

I had a bunch of keys to play with, as long as I was capable only of pleasure in what glittered and jingled; as I grew older, I had a cart, and a ball; and when I was five or six years old, two boxes of well-cut wooden bricks. With these modest, but, I still think, entirely sufficient possessions, and being always summarily whipped if I cried, did not do as I was bid, or tumbled on the stairs, I soon attained serene and secure methods of life and motion; and could pass my days contentedly in tracing the squares and comparing the colours of my carpet; – examining the knots in the wood of the floor, or counting the bricks in the opposite houses.

John Ruskin: PRAETERITA

It is an anxious, sometimes a dangerous thing to be a doll. Dolls cannot choose; they can only be chosen; they cannot 'do'; they can only be done by; children who do not understand this often do wrong things, and then the dolls are hurt and abused and lost; and when this happens dolls cannot speak, nor do anything except be hurt and abused and lost. If you have any dolls, you should remember that.

Rumer Godden: THE DOLL'S HOUSE

CHILDHOOD

I am called Childhood, in play is all my mind,
To cast a quoit, a cockstele, and a ball;
A top can I set, and drive in its kind;
But would to God these hateful bookes all
Were in a fire burnt to ponder* small!
Then might I lead my life always in play,
Which life God send me to mine endying day.

Sir Thomas More

* a small amount

Here we go round the mulberry bush,
The mulberry bush, the mulberry bush,
Here we go round the mulberry bush,
On a cold and frosty morning.

SEVEN THINGS TO DO

Turn on the tap for straight and silver water in the sink,
Cross your finger through
The sleek thread falling.
– *One*

Spread white sandgrains on a tray,
And make clean furrows with a bent stick
To stare for a meaning.
– *Two*

Draw some clumsy birds on yellow paper,
Confronting each other and as if to fly
Over your scribbled hill.
– *Three*

Cut rapid holes into folded paper, look
At the unfolded pattern, look
Through the unfolded pattern.
– *Four*

Walk on any square stone of the pavement,
Or on any crack between,
Counting your careful paces.
– *Five*

Throw up a ball to touch the truest brick
Of the red–brick wall,
Catch it with neat, cupped hands.
– *Six*

Make up in your head a path, and name it,
Name where it will lead you,
Walk towards where it will lead you.
– *Seven*

One, two, three, four, five, six, seven:
Take-up-the-rag-doll-quietly-and-sing-her-to-sleep.

Alan Brownjohn

THE RAG DOLL TO THE HEEDLESS CHILD

I love you
with my linen heart.

You cannot
know how these

rigid, lumpy arms
shudder in your grasp,

or what
tears dam up against

these blue eye-smudges at
your capriciousness.

At night I watch you sleep;
you'll never know

how I thrust my face
into the stream

of your warm breath;
and how

love-words choke me behind
this sewn-up mouth.

David Harsent

THE DOLL'S HOUSE

Open the doors
and let your little fat pinkies
prowl through these rooms.

There is no cellar
with dark stairs
to frighten the children.

It is a house
with no roots at all.
Come into the hall

and tap the barometer
that hangs on the wall.
It will neither rise nor fall.

In the kitchen
you will touch
the little red paper fire

that glows in the range,
then put your finger
to your mouth

and make a show
of being burned.
They all do.

And you may,
if you will,
mumble my wooden food.

Upstairs, in the bedroom,
you will not fail
to lift up the pretty valance

and find
to your feigned
and loud delight

that there is indeed
a guzunder there.
For this is an old house

and as its ways
are not your ways,
improprieties

are of no account.
But when you find me
and try to lift me,

as I know you will,
you will find
that someone –

oh, it was years ago –
thought fit to stitch me
into my chair.

Neil Curry

RUSSIAN DOLL

When I held you up to my cheek you were cold
when I came close to your smile it dissolved,

the paint on your lips was as deep
as the steaming ruby of beetroot soup

but your breath smelled of varnish and pine
and your eyes swivelled away from mine.

When I wanted to open you up
you glowed, dumpy and perfect

smoothing your dozen little selves
like rolls of fat under your apron

and I hadn't the heart to look at them.
I knew I would be spoiling something.

But when I listened to your heart
I heard the worlds inside of you spinning
like the earth on its axis spinning.

Helen Dunmore

Baby, my dolly, oh, she never cries!
Lie still, my darling, and close little eyes!
Mother must go, dear, and look for the others –
All the dear sisters, and all the dear brothers.

THE BROKEN DOLL

All the bells were ringing,
And all the birds were singing,
When Molly sat down crying
  For her broken doll:
  O you silly Moll!
Sobbing and sighing
  For a broken doll,
When all the bells are ringing,
And all the birds are singing.

Christina Rossetti

SONG OF THE HAT-RAISING DOLL

I raise my hat
And lower it.
As I unwind
I slow a bit.
This life—
I make a go of it
But tick-tock time
I know of it.

Yes, tick-tock time
I know of it.
I fear the final
O of it,
But making
A brave show of it
I raise my hat
And lower it.

John Mole

LAW AND JUSTICE

Now, this is Mary Queen of Scots!
  Push all her curls away;
For we have heard about her plots,
  And she must die to-day.

What's this? I MUST NOT HURT HER SO;
  YOU LOVE HER DEARLY STILL;
YOU THINK SHE WILL BE GOOD? – Oh, no!
  I say she never will.

My own new saw, & made of steel!
  Oh, silly child to cry;
She's only wood, she cannot feel,
  And, look, her eyes are dry.

Her cheeks are bright with rosy spots;
  I know she cares for none—
Besides, she's Mary, Queen of Scots
  And so it MUST be done!

Jean Ingelow

THE LOST DOLL

I once had a sweet little doll, dears,
　The prettiest doll in the world;
Her cheeks were so red and so white, dears,
　And her hair was so charmingly curled.
But I lost my poor little doll, dears,
　As I played in the heath one day;
And I cried for her more than a week, dears;
　But I never could find where she lay.

I found my poor little doll, dears,
　As I played in the heath one day:
Folks say she is terribly changed, dears,
　For her paint is all washed away,
And her arm trodden off by the cows, dears,
　And her hair not the least bit curled:
Yet for old sakes' sake she is still, dears,
　The prettiest doll in the world.

Charles Kingsley

THE DOLLS

'Whenever you dress me dolls, mammy,
  Why do you dress them so,
And make them gallant soldiers,
  When never a one I know;
And not as gentle ladies
  With frills and frocks and curls,
As people dress the dollies
  Of other little girls?'

Ah – why did she not answer:–
  'Because your mammy's heed
Is always gallant soldiers,
  As well may be, indeed.
One of them was your daddy,
  His name I must not tell;
He's not the dad who lives here,
  But one I love too well.'

Thomas Hardy

THE DUMB SOLDIER

When the grass was closely mown,
Walking on the lawn alone,
In the turf a hole I found
And hid a soldier underground.

Spring and daisies came apace;
Grasses hide my hiding-place;
Grasses run like a green sea
O'er the lawn up to my knee.

Under grass alone he lies,
Looking up with leaden eyes,
Scarlet coat and pointed gun,
To the stars and to the sun.

When the grass is ripe like grain,
When the scythe is stoned again,
When the lawn is shaven clear,
Then my hole shall reappear.

I shall find him, never fear,
I shall find my grenadier;
But for all that's gone and come,
I shall find my soldier dumb.

He has lived, a little thing,
In the grassy woods of spring;
Done, if he could tell me true,
Just as I should like to do.

He has seen the starry hours
And the springing of the flowers;
And the fairy things that pass
In the forests of the grass.

In the silence he has heard
Talking bee and ladybird,
And the butterfly has flown
O'er him as he lay alone.

Not a word will he disclose,
Not a word of all he knows.
I must lay him on the shelf,
And make up the tale myself.

Robert Louis Stevenson

TO AN INFANT

Ah cease thy Tears and Sobs, my little Life!
I did but snatch away the unclasp'd Knife:
Some safer Toy will soon arrest thine eye,
And to quick Laughter change this peevish cry!
Poor Stumbler on the rocky coast of Woe,
Tutor'd by Pain each source of Pain to know!
Alike the foodful fruit and scorching fire
Awake thy eager grasp and young desire:
Alike the Good, the Ill offend thy sight,
And rouse the stormy Sense of shrill Affright!
Untaught, yet wise! mid all thy brief alarms
Thou closely clingest to thy Mother's arms,
Nestling thy little face in that fond breast
Whose anxious Heavings lull thee to thy rest!
Man's breathing Miniature! thou mak'st me sigh—
A Babe art thou – and such a Thing am I!

Samuel Taylor Coleridge

THE TOYS

My little Son, who look'd from thoughtful eyes
And moved and spoke in quiet grown-up wise,
Having my law the seventh time disobey'd,
I struck him, and dismiss'd
With hard words and unkiss'd,
His Mother, who was patient, being dead.
Then, fearing lest his grief should hinder sleep,
I visited his bed,
But found him slumbering deep,
With darken'd eyelids, and their lashes yet
From his late sobbing wet.
And I, with moan,
Kissing away his tears, left others of my own;
For, on a table drawn beside his head,
He had put, within his reach,
A box of counters and a red-vein'd stone,
A piece of glass abraded by the beach
And six or seven shells,
A bottle with bluebells
And two French copper coins, ranged there with
                                        careful art,
To comfort his sad heart.

So when that night I pray'd
To God, I wept, and said:
Ah, when at last we lie with tranced breath,
Not vexing Thee in death,
And Thou rememberest of what toys
We made our joys,
How weakly understood,
Thy great commanded good,
Then, fatherly not less
Than I whom Thou hast moulded from the clay,

Thou'lt leave Thy wrath, and say,
'I will be sorry for their childishness.'

Coventry Patmore

from SUMMONED BY BELLS

Safe were those evenings of the pre-war world
When firelight shone on green linoleum;
I heard the church bells hollowing out the sky,
Deep beyond deep, like never-ending stars,
And turned to Archibald, my safe old bear,
Whose woollen eyes looked sad or glad at me,
Whose ample forehead I could wet with tears,
Whose half-moon ears received my confidence,
Who made me laugh, who never let me down.
I used to wait for hours to see him move,
Convinced that he could breathe. One dreadful day
They hid him from me as a punishment:
Sometimes the desolation of that loss
Comes back to me and I must go upstairs
To see him in the sawdust, so to speak,
Safe and returned to his idolator.

John Betjeman

ORIGINAL TIN

The sky is tin, the street is tin, and
now a tin man, red and yellow walking as a spring unwinds.
His two halves do not fit exactly but
he perseveres, and finds a house of tin on which are printed
red bricks, blue windows, and the picture of a door
at which he knocks (no answer), says in his tin voice,
'I'm here,' then enters.
Now his face is printed on the printed windows,
looking out past slanting lines of white. 'I'm here,'
he says in his tin voice, and notes the rattling of the sky.

Russell Hoban

THE TIN FROG

I have hopped, when properly wound up, the whole length
of the hallway; once hopped halfway down the stairs, and fell.
Since then the two halves of my tin have been awry;
    my strength
is not quite what it used to be; I do not hop so well.

Russell Hoban

TIN WHEELS

They were the very first of my found things.
Two little wheels, joined by a metal rod,
Part of a cheap tin toy; all small enough
To huddle hidden in a toddler's hand.
I loved them dearly for their jolly roundness
Giggling along the flags at a finger-push.
I loved the having and the keeping-safe
Of this, the first fruit of my own finding.

An adult found the rust and the sharp edges.

I still recall the day I found them gone
And what was said. Even now, in lost nights
When I have 'nothing better to cry for'
I wail as I did then:
'Gran says you threw my little wheels away'.

They were the last love that I never hid;
They were my first irrevocable loss.

Ann Drysdale

THE DEAD BIRD

Ah, that was but the wind
Your soft down stirred,
O bird, lying with sidelong head;
These open eyes are blind,
I cannot frighten you away;
You are so very dead
I almost say
'You are not a dead *bird*.'

Andrew Young

A BIRD IN THE HOUSE

It was a yellow voice, a high, shrill treble in the nursery
White always and high, I remember it so,
White cupboard, off-white table, mugs, dolls' faces
And I was four or five. The garden could have been
Miles away. We were taken down to the green
Asparagus beds, the cut lawn, and the smell of it
Comes each summer after rain when white returns. Our bird,
A canary called Peter, sang behind bars. The black and white cat
Curled and snoozed by the fire and danger was far away.

Far away for us. Safety was life and only now do I know
That white walls and lit leaves knocking windows
Are a good prison but always you have
To escape, fly off from love not felt as love,
But our bird died in his yellow feathers. The quick
Cat caught him, tore him through bars when we were out
And I do not remember tears or sadness, I only
Remember the ritual, the warm yellow feathers we put
In a cardboard egg. What a sense of fitness. How far, I know now,
Ritual goes back, egg to egg, birth to burial and we went
Down the garden softly, two in a small procession,
And the high clouds bent down, the sky pulled aside
Its blue curtains. Death was there or else
Where the wise cat had hidden. That day we buried our bird
With a sense of fitness, not knowing death would be hard
Later, dark, without form or purpose.
After my first true grief I wept, was sad, was dark, but today,
Clear of terror and agony,
The yellow bird sings in my mind and I say
That the child is callous but wise, knows the purpose of play.
And the grief of ten years ago
Now has an ancient rite,
A walk down the garden carrying death in an egg

And the sky singing, the trees still waving farewell
When dying was nothing to know.

Elizabeth Jennings

ANN, UPON THE STROKE OF THREE

Ann, upon the stroke of three,
Half-way 'twixt dinner-time and tea,
Cosily tucked in her four-legged chair,
With nice clean hands and smooth brushed hair,
In some small secret nursery nook,
Sits with her big Picture-book.

There Puss in Boots, with sidelong eye
And bushy tail goes mincing by;

Peering into an empty cupboard
With her old Dog stoops Mother Hubbard;

Beside a bushy bright-green Wood
Walks with the Wolf Red Ridinghood;

In their small cottage the Three Bears,
Each at his bowl of Porridge stares;

There's striking Clock – and scampering Mouse;
The King of Hearts' cool Counting-house;

There a Fine Lady rides all day,
But never, never rides away;

While Jack and Jill for ever roll;
And drinks to his Fiddlers Old King Cole.

And though Ann's little busy head
Can't quite get down from A to Z,
She is content to sit and look
At her bright-coloured Picture-book.

Walter de la Mare

Hickory Dickory Dock!
The mouse ran up the clock.
The clock struck One!
The mouse ran down!
Hickory Dickory Dock!

ANNE AND THE FIELD-MOUSE

We found a mouse in the chalk quarry today
In a circle of stones and empty oil drums
By the fag ends of a fire. There had been
A picnic there; he must have been after the crumbs.

Jane saw him first, a flicker of brown fur
In and out of the charred wood and chalk-white.
I saw him last, but not till we'd turned up
Every stone and surprised him into flight,

Though not far – little zigzag spurts from stone
To stone. Once, as he lurked in his hiding-place,
I saw his beady eyes uplifted to mine.
I'd never seen such terror in so small a face.

I watched, amazed and guilty. Beside us suddenly
A heavy pheasant whirred up from the ground,
Scaring us all; and, before we knew it, the mouse
Had broken cover, skimming away without a sound,

Melting into the nettles. We didn't go
Till I'd chalked in capitals on a rusty can:
THERE'S A MOUSE IN THOSE NETTLES. LEAVE
HIM ALONE. NOVEMBER 15th. ANNE.

Ian Serraillier

THE OTHER CHILD

When I put her in the swing
And set it going while I sing,
And all the apple-leaves of June
Shake in keeping with my tune,

And she cries merrily, sweet and shrill,
'Higher, higher, higher still!'—
Seated on an apple-limb,
Invisible as air,
Watching this child bird-like skim
The speckled world of shade and sun,
Another child is there.

And every time my song is done,
This one, with her innocent brow
And blue eyes almost clear of fun,
Says, It is her turn now!
Lift me down and put her in,
And *I'll* sit on the apple-tree—
And then once over I begin
My song to sing
And rock the swing,
Where only I and this child see
Flying through the speckled air
The other child who's always there.

Eleanor Farjeon

THE SWING

How do you like to go up in a swing,
   Up in the air so blue?
Oh, I do think it the pleasantest thing
   Ever a child can do!

Up in the air and over the wall,
   Till I can see so wide,
Rivers and trees and cattle and all
   Over the countryside –

Till I look down on the garden green,
   Down on the roof so brown –
Up in the air I go flying again,
   Up in the air and down!

Robert Louis Stevenson

LAURA ROUND AND ROUND

When Laura turns five cartwheels, long legs flashing,
firm hands walking green grass round her head,
bare feet singing blue sky as they tread
heavens below her, earth above her going,
all its daisies downward on her growing,
all its summer whirling with her smile—
Laura, upside-down, turns for a little while
whole worlds right side up.

Russell Hoban

SEVEN TIMES ONE

THERE's no dew left on the daisies and clover,
  There's no rain left in heaven:
I've said my 'seven times' over and over,
  Seven times one are seven.

I am old, so old, I can write a letter;
  My birthday lessons are done:
The lambs play always, they know no better;
  They are only one times one.

O moon! in the night I have seen you sailing
  And shining so round and low;
You were bright! ah bright! but your light is failing—
  You are nothing now but a bow.

You moon, have you done something wrong in heaven
  That God has hidden your face?
I hope if you have you will soon be forgiven,
  And shine again in your place.

O velvet bee, you're a dusty fellow,
  You've powdered your legs with gold!
O brave marsh marybuds, rich and yellow,
  Give me your money to hold!

O columbine, open your folded wrapper,
  Where two twin turtle-doves dwell!
O cuckoo-pint, toll me the purple clapper
  That hangs in your clear green bell!

And show me your nest with the young ones in it;
  I will not steal them away;
I am old! you may trust me, linnet, linnet—
  I am seven times one to-day.

Jean Ingelow

A CHILD'S LAUGHTER

All the bells of heaven may ring,
All the birds of heaven may sing,
All the wells on earth may spring,
All the winds on earth may bring
   All sweet sounds together;
Sweeter far than all things heard,
Hand of harper, tone of bird,
Sound of woods at sundawn stirred,
Welling water's winsome word,
   Wind in warm wan weather,

One thing yet there is, that none
Hearing ere its chime be done
Knows not well the sweetest one
Heard of man beneath the sun,
   Hoped in heaven hereafter;
Soft and strong and loud and light,
Very sound of very light
Heard from morning's rosiest height,
When the soul of all delight
   Fills a child's clear laughter.

Golden bells of welcome rolled
Never forth such notes, nor told
Hours so blithe in tones so bold,
As the radiant mouth of gold
   Here that rings forth heaven.
If the golden-crested wren
Were a nightingale – why, then,
Something seen and heard of men
Might be half as sweet as when
   Laughs a child of seven.

Algernon Charles Swinburne

WHEN I WAS YOUR AGE

When I was your age, child –
When I was eight,
When I was ten,
When I was two
(How old are you?) –
When I was your age, child,
My father would have gone quite *wild*
Had I behaved the way you
Do.
What, food uneaten on my plate
When I was eight?
What, room in such a filthy state
When I was ten?
What, late
For school when I was two?
My father would have shouted, 'When
I was your age, child, my father would have *raved*
Had I behaved
The way you
Do.'

When I was
Your age, child, I did not drive us
All perpetually mad
By bashing
Up my little brother and reducing him to tears.
There was a war on in those years!
There were no brothers to be had!
Even sisters were on ration!
My goodness, we were pleased
To get *anything* to tease!
We were glad
Of aunts and dogs,

Of chickens, grandmothers, and frogs;
Of creatures finned and creatures hooved,
And second cousins twice removed!

When I was your
Age, child, I was more
Considerate of others
(Particularly of fathers and of mothers).
I did not sprawl
Reading the *Dandy*
Or the *Beano*
When aunts and uncles came to call.
Indeed no.
I grandly
Entertained them all
With 'Please' and 'Thank you,' 'May I...?'
  'Thank you,' 'Sorry,' 'Please,'
And other remarks like these.
And if a chance came in the conversation
I would gracefully recite a line
Which everyone recognized as a quotation
From one of the higher multiplication
Tables, like 'Seven sevens are forty-nine.'

When I was your age, child, I
Should never have dreamed
Of sitting idly
Watching television half the night.
It would have seemed
Demented:
Television not then having been
Invented.

When I
Was your age, child, I did not lie
About
The house all day.

(I did not lie about anything at all – no liar I!)
I got out!
I ran away
To sea!
(Though naturally I was back, with hair brushed and hands
    washed, in time for tea.)
Oh yes, goodness me,
When I was nine
I had worked already down a diamond mine,
And fought in several minor wars,
And hunted boars
In the lonelier
Parts of Patagonia.
(Though I admit that possibly by then
I was getting on for ten.)
In the goldfields of Australia
I learned the bitterness of failure;
Experience in the temples of Siam
Made me the wise and punctual man I am;
But the lesson that I value most
I learned upon the Coromandel Coast –
Never, come what may, to boast.

When
I was your age, child, and the older generation
Offered now and then
A kindly explanation
Of what the world was like in their young day
I did not yawn in that rude way.
Why, goodness me,
There being no television to see
(As I have, I think, already said)
We were dashed grateful
For any entertainment we could get instead,
However tedious and hateful.

So grow up, child! And be
Your age! (What *is* your age, then?
Eight? Or nine? Or two? Or ten?)
Remember, as you look at me –
When I was your age I was forty-three.

Michael Frayn

THE MORNING WALK

When Anne and I go out a walk,
We hold each other's hand and talk
Of all the things we mean to do
When Anne and I are forty-two.

And when we've thought about a thing,
Like bowling hoops or bicycling,
Or falling down on Anne's balloon,
We do it in the afternoon.

A. A. Milne

3 · *The darkening garden*

'No, no not hide and seek,' Lucy thought to herself. 'Oh God,' she prayed rapidly, 'let it not be hide and seek. Please, dear God, let it not be hide and seek.' But it was...now Lucy must face it, this thing that she dreaded most...Hiding was bad enough, waiting behind a door, holding your breath, fearing that a groping hand might suddenly touch you, a triumphant voice shriek, 'Here she is!' But how much worse were the flight and pursuit: feet running behind, drawing nearer every minute. Useless to say that this was only Maurice or Delia after you, worse than useless, because at bottom you knew that it was something really dreadful, something infinitely disasterous that would catch you in the end, however fast you ran...

Now she must find a place to hide in before Delia should have finished counting a hundred...there was the potato-house: few people would think of looking there; on the other hand, if they did (and Delia had a way of reading her thoughts) she would be caught like a mouse in a trap in that dark place, smelling of earth, with no more than a streak of yellow daylight showing through the crack in the door.

Eiluned Lewis: DEW ON THE GRASS

Between the dark and the daylight,
   when the night is beginning to lower,
Comes a pause in the day's occupation
   that is known as the Children's Hour...

H. W. Longfellow: THE CHILDREN'S HOUR

BOY IN THE DUSK

I will make a small statue
  of a boy to-day,
that will half look at you
  and half away.

I will have him standing
  in darkness, but
he will be pretending
  that he is not.

I will give him a fiddle,
  and he will not know
that it broke in the middle
  long ago.

His lips will be parted
  as though he smiled
with the broken-hearted
  grace of a child.

And many will wonder,
  and some will ask,
what I mean by my slender
  'Boy in the Dusk.'

'Is he beauty deserted?
  Vision betrayed?
Or a love that started,
  and was afraid?'

'Is he love like a ghost
  In the valley of death?
Or youth that is lost
  and remembereth?'

But I will not name him,
   and every man
must find and acclaim him
   as he can.

Since from childish and small things
   the Boy in the Dusk
may flash into all things
   the heart can ask.

Or he may be only
   a small bronze statue
of a boy, who is lonely,
   and looks half at you.

Humbert Wolfe

LOOK, EDWIN!

Look, Edwin! Do you see that boy
Talking to the other boy?
No, over there by those two men—
Wait, don't look now—now look again.
No, not the one in navy-blue;
That's the one he's talking to.
Sure you see him? Stripèd pants?
Well, *he was born in Paris, France.*

Edna St Vincent Millay

BOY AT THE WINDOW

Seeing the snowman standing all alone
In dusk and cold is more than he can bear.
The small boy weeps to hear the wind prepare
A night of gnashings and enormous moan.
His tearful sight can hardly reach to where
The pale-faced figure with bitumen eyes
Returns him such a god-forsaken stare
As outcast Adam gave to Paradise.

The man of snow is, nonetheless, content,
Having no wish to go inside and die.
Still, he is moved to see the youngster cry.
Though frozen water is his element,
He melts enough to drop from one soft eye
A trickle of the purest rain, a tear
For the child at the bright pane surrounded by
Such warmth, such light, such love, and so much fear.

Richard Wilbur

Why should we fear that which we cannot fly?
Fear is more pain than is the pain it fears...

Sir Philip Sydney

RISING FIVE

'I'm rising five,' he said,
'Not four,' and little coils of hair
Un-clicked themselves upon his head.
His spectacles, brimful of eyes to stare
At me and the meadow, reflected cones of light
Above his toffee-buckled cheeks. He'd been alive
Fifty-six months or perhaps a week more:

                     not four,
But rising five.

Around him in the field the cells of spring
Bubbled and doubled; buds unbuttoned; shoot
And stem shook out the creases from their frills,
And every tree was swilled with green.
It was the season after blossoming,
Before the forming of the fruit:

            not May,
But rising June.

                 And in the sky
The dust dissected the tangential light:

            not day,
But rising night;

      not now,
But rising soon.

The new buds push the old leaves from the bough.
We drop our youth behind us like a boy
Throwing away his toffee-wrappers. We never see the flower,
But only the fruit in the flower; never the fruit,
But only the rot in the fruit. We look for the marriage bed
In the baby's cradle, we look for the grave in the bed:

               not living,
But rising dead.

Norman Nicholson

MY SHADOW

I have a little shadow that goes in and out with me,
And what can be the use of him is more than I can see.
He is very, very like me from the heels up to the head;
And I see him jump before me, when I jump into my bed.

The funniest thing about him is the way he likes to grow –
Not at all like proper children, which is always very slow;
For he sometimes shoots up taller like an india-rubber ball,
And he sometimes gets so little that there's none of him at all.

He hasn't got a notion of how children ought to play,
And can only make a fool of me in every sort of way.
He stays so close beside me, he's a coward you can see;
I'd think shame to stick to nursie as that shadow sticks to me!

One morning, very early, before the sun was up,
I rose and found the shining dew on every buttercup;
But my lazy little shadow, like an arrant sleepy-head,
Had stayed at home behind me and was fast asleep in bed.

Robert Louis Stevenson

Some there be that shadows kiss
Such have but a shadow's bliss.

William Shakespeare

THE SHADOW

When the last of gloaming's gone,
When the world is drowned in Night,
Then swims up the great round Moon,
Washing with her borrowed light
Twig, stone, grass-blade – pin-point bright –
Every tiniest thing in sight.

Then, on tiptoe,
Off go I
To a white-washed
Wall near by,
Where, for secret
Company,
My small shadow
Waits for me.

Still and stark,
Or stirring – so,
All I'm doing
He'll do too.
Quieter than
A cat he mocks
My walk, my gestures,
Clothes and looks.

I twist and turn,
I creep, I prowl,
Likewise does he,
The crafty soul,
The Moon for lamp,
And for music, owl.

'Sst!' I whisper,
'Shadow, come!'

No answer:
He is blind and dumb –
Blind and dumb.
And when I go,
The wall will stand empty,
White as snow.

Walter de la Mare

THE CHILD AND THE SHADOW

Your shadow I have seen you play with often.
O and it seems a shadow light before you,
Glittering behind you. You can see what lies
Beneath its marking dappled on the water
    Or on the earth a footprint merely;
No total darkness is cast by your body.

Say that it is a game of identities this –
You chasing yourself not caring whatever you find.
You have not sought a use for mirrors yet,
It is not your own shadow that you watch,
    Only our world which you learn slowly:
Our shadows strive to mingle with your own,

Chase them, then, as you chase the leaves or a bird,
Disturb us, disturb us, still let the light lie gently
Under the place that you carve for yourself in air;
Look, the fish are darting beneath your reflection
    But you see deep beyond your glance:
It is our shadow that slides in between.

Elizabeth Jennings

SHADOWS IN THE WATER

In unexperienc'd Infancy
Many a sweet Mistake doth ly:
Mistake tho false, intending tru;
A *Seeming* somwhat more than *View*;
   That doth instruct the Mind
   In Things that ly behind,
And many Secrets to us show
Which afterwards we com to know.

Thus did I by the Water's brink
Another World beneath me think;
And while the lofty spacious Skies
Reversed there abus'd mine Eys,
   I fancy'd other Feet
   Came mine to touch and meet;
As by som Puddle I did play
Another World within it lay.

Beneath the Water Peeple drown'd.
Yet with another Hev'n crown'd,
In spacious Regions seem'd to go
Freely moving to and fro:
   In bright and open Space
   I saw their very face;
Eys, Hands, and Feet they had like mine;
Another Sun did with them shine.

'Twas strange that Peeple there should walk,
And yet I could not hear them talk:
That throu a little watry Chink,
Which one dry Ox or Horse might drink,
   We other Worlds should see,
   Yet not admitted be;

And other Confines there behold
Of Light and Darkness, Heat and Cold.

I call'd them oft, but call'd in vain;
No Speeches we could entertain:
Yet did I there expect to find
Som other World, to pleas my Mind.
   I plainly saw by these
   A new *Antipodes*,
Whom, tho they were so plainly seen,
A Film kept off that stood between.

O ye that stand upon the Brink,
Whom I so near me, throu the Chink,
With Wonder see: What Faces there,
Whose Feet, whose Bodies, do ye wear?
   I my Companions see
   In You, another Me.
They seemed Others, but are We;
Our second Selvs those Shadows be.

Of all the Play-mates which I knew
That here I do the Image view
In other Selvs; what can it mean?
But that below the purling Stream
   Som unknown Joys there be
   Laid up in Store for me;
To which I shall, when that thin Skin
Is broken, be admitted in.

Thomas Traherne

SEEKING

When little Jane lifts up her head,
  Uncovering her eyes,
Every other child has fled
  Into the mysteries.
The playmates that she knew are gone,
  And Jane is left alone.

Oh Alice with the starry looks,
  Oh Ann with gleaming curls,
What dusky corners, what dim nooks
  Have hid you little girls?
The house is vast and Jane is small,
  And are you here at all?

Oh Richard with the flashing smile,
  Oh Rob with freckled brow,
Where are you hiding all this while,
  You who were here but now?
The house lies in a sleep as deep
  As Sleeping Beauty's sleep.

Through all the rooms grown deaf and blind
  Jane seeks with throbbing heart
The hidden playmates whom to find
  Will make small tremors start —
For when she finds them in the game
  They may not be the same.

Eleanor Farjeon

HIDE AND SEEK

Call out. Call loud: 'I'm ready! Come and find me!'
The sacks in the toolshed smell like the seaside.
They'll never find you in this salty dark,
But be careful that your feet aren't sticking out.
Wiser not to risk another shout.
The floor is cold. They'll probably be searching
The bushes near the swing. Whatever happens
You mustn't sneeze when they come prowling in.
And here they are, whispering at the door;
You've never heard them sound so hushed before.
Don't breathe. Don't move. Stay dumb. Hide in
    your blindness.
They're moving closer, someone stumbles, mutters;
Their words and laughter scuffle, and they're gone.
But don't come out just yet; they'll try the lane
And then the greenhouse and back here again.
They must be thinking that you're very clever,
Getting more puzzled as they search all over.
It seems a long time since they went away.
Your legs are stiff, the cold bites through your coat;
The dark damp smell of sand moves in your throat.
It's time to let them know that you're the winner.
Push off the sacks. Uncurl and stretch. That's better!
Out of the shed and call to them: 'I've won!
Here I am! Come and own up I've caught you!'
The darkening garden watches. Nothing stirs.
The bushes hold their breath; the sun is gone.
Yes, here you are. But where are they who sought
    you?

Vernon Scannell

BROTHER AND SISTER SONNETS

I cannot choose but think upon the time
When our two lives grew like two buds that kiss
At lightest thrill from the bee's swinging chime,
Because the one so near the other is.
He was the elder and a little man
Of forty inches, bound to show no dread,
And I the girl that puppy-like now ran,
Now lagged behind my brother's larger tread.
I held him wise, and when he talked to me
Of snakes and birds, and which God loved the best,
I thought his knowledge marked the boundary
Where men grew blind, though angels knew the rest.
  If he said 'Hush!' I tried to hold my breath
    Wherever he said 'Come!' I stepped in faith.

We had the self-same world enlarged for each
By loving difference of girl and boy:
The fruit that hung on high beyond my reach
He plucked for me, and oft he must employ
A measuring glance to guide my tiny shoe
Where lay firm stepping-stones, or call to mind
'This thing I like my sister may not do,
For she is little, and I must be kind.'
Thus boyish Will the nobler mastery learned
Where inward vision over impulse reigns,
Widening its life with separate life discerned,
A Like unlike, a Self that self restrains.
  His years with others must the sweeter be
    For those brief days he spent in loving me.

His sorrow was my sorrow, and his joy
Sent little leaps and laughs through all my frame;
My doll seemed lifeless and no girlish toy
Had any reason when my brother came.
I knelt with him at marbles, marked his fling
Cut the ringed stem and make the apple drop,
Or watched him winding close the spiral string
That looped the orbits of the humming top.
Grasped by such fellowship my vagrant thought
Ceased with dream-fruit dream-wishes to fulfil;
My aëry-picturing fantasy was taught
Subjection to the harder, truer skill
   That seeks with deeds to grave a thought-tracked line,
   And by 'What is', 'What will be' to define.

School parted us; we never found again
That childish world where our two spirits mingled
Like scents from varying roses that remain
One sweetness, nor can evermore be singled.
Yet the twin habit of that early time
Lingered for long about the heart and tongue:
We had been natives of one happy clime,
And its dear accent to our utterance clung.
Till the dire years whose awful name is Change
Had grasped our souls still yearning in divorce,
And pitiless shaped them in two forms that range
Two elements which sever their life's course.
   But were another childhood-world my share,
   I would be born a little sister there.

George Eliot

A BIRD'S-EYE VIEW

Quoth the boy, 'I'll climb that tree,
  And bring down a nest I know.'
Quoth the girl, 'I will not see
  Little birds defrauded so.
Cowardly their nests to take,
And their little hearts to break,
And their little eggs to steal,
  Leave them happy for my sake,—
Surely little birds can feel.'

Quoth the boy, 'My senses whirl;
  Until now I never heard
Of the wisdom of a girl
  Or the feelings of a bird!
Pretty Mrs Solomon,
Tell me what you reckon on
When you prate in such a strain;
  If I wring their necks anon,
Certainly they might feel—pain!'

Quoth the girl, 'I watch them talk,
  Making love and making fun,
In the pretty ash-tree walk,
  When my daily task is done.
In their little eyes I find
They are very fond and kind.
Every change of song or voice,
  Plainly proveth to my mind,
They can suffer and rejoice.'

And the little Robin-bird,
  (Nice brown back and crimson breast)
All the conversation heard
  Sitting trembling in his nest.

'What a world' he cried 'of bliss,
Full of birds and girls were this!
Blithe we'd answer to their call;
   But a great mistake it is
Boys were ever made at all.'

Menella Bute Smedley & Elizabeth Anna Hart

THE THRUSH'S NEST

Within a thick and spreading hawthorn bush
   That overhung a mole-hill large and round,
I heard from morn to morn a merry thrush
   Sing hymns to sunrise, and I drank the sound
With joy; and, often an intruding guest,
   I watched her secret toils from day to day—
How true she warped the moss to form a nest,
   And modelled it within with wood and clay;
And by and by, like heath-bells gilt with dew,
   There lay her shining eggs, as bright as flowers,
Ink-spotted over shells of greeny blue;
   And there I witnessed, in the sunny hours,
A brood of nature's minstrels chirp and fly,
Glad as that sunshine and the laughing sky.

John Clare

SONG

I had a dove and the sweet dove died;
  And I have thought it died of grieving:
O, what could it grieve for? Its feet were tied,
  With a silken thread of my own hand's weaving;
Sweet little red feet! why should you die—
Why should you leave me, sweet bird! why?
You liv'd alone in the forest-tree,
Why, pretty thing! would you not live with me?
I kiss'd you oft and gave you white peas;
Why not live sweetly, as in the green trees?

John Keats

REVELATION

We make ourselves a place apart
  Behind light words that tease and flout,
But oh, the agitated heart
  Till someone really find us out.

'Tis pity if the case require
  (Or so we say) that in the end
We speak the literal to inspire
  The understanding of a friend.

But so with all, from babes that play
  At hide-and-seek to God afar,
So all who hide too well away
  Must speak and tell us where they are.

Robert Frost

THE NOISE THAT TIME MAKES

The noise that Time makes in passing by
Is very slight but even you can hear it,
Having not necessarily to be near it,
Needing only the slightest will to try:
Hold the receiver of a telephone
To your ear when no-one is talking on the line
And what may at first sound to you like the whine
Of wind over distant wires is Time's own
Garments brushing against a windy cloud.
That same noise again but not so well
May be heard by taking a small cockle-shell
From the sand and holding it against your head;
Then you can hear Time's footsteps as they pass
Over the earth brushing the eternal grass.

Merrill Moore

THE CHILD AND THE SHELL

                                    I have seen
A curious child, who dwelt upon a tract
Of inland ground, applying to his ear
The convolutions of a smooth-lipped shell;
To which, in silence hushed, his very soul
Listened intensely; and his countenance soon
Brightened with joy; for from within were heard
Murmurings, whereby the monitor expressed
Mysterious union with its native sea.
Even such a shell the universe itself
Is to the ear of Faith.

William Wordsworth

LITTLE DOLLY DAYDREAM

Her mother's out today,
the house is quiet as a dozing mouse,
the cat meows and curls to sleep.

Upstairs she stands before the glass,
arms on hips, she struts this way and that.

Laid out beneath the looking-glass are jars or boxes,
bottles, aerosols and plastic packs.

She has an hour to try on all the scents,
to puff the clouding powder, smear the cream
and draw whatever feature her changing fancy takes.

The placid pool invites, and plunging in dissolves
her ordinary self – the bitten nails, the grimy neck,
the whisps of wayward hair.

She lifts the little brush and gently strokes,
stardusts the tickling eyelids with some silver flakes,
daubs in bow lips and high-arched brows.

Deftly, having watched, sticks lashes.
Drooping minute frayed bats' wings,
glistens lipsalve, reddens cheeks.

She turns her pale child's face
into all the faces she has seen
in the darker mirrors of her mind.

Stringing out her loosening strands of hair,
she transforms herself into a witch,
the Snow White Queen,

La Belle Dame Sans Merci,
a coyly smiling Columbine.

And, from lurking deeps beyond the silver wall,
she conjures, unaware,
the many quickly-fading future selves
the unkind glass conceals.

Barry Maybury

THE GRANDSON DRESSES UP

James painted black moustaches round his nose,
And in the glass a sneering Satan smiled.
I thought once more how harrowingly glows
Beneath the cork the innocence of a child.

Frances Cornford

LET'S PRETEND

You shall be the father,
I, the mother,
unless you would rather
we played some other
dressing-up game,
say, bride and groom,
putting on the same
clothes in another
part of the room;
I must have a veil,
you shall marry me
upon the first of May,
then we will live happily
ever after, but today
I am going to wear a crown
and be a queen
with long, trailing gown,
dance to the tambourine;
you shall be a king,
clap hands and sing.
And when I wear
black cloak and hat,
gold ring with diamond,
I will change you into a bear
or witches' cat
with my magic wand.
Before you can say Jack Robinson
I shall fly in my aeroplane
one hundred miles, a million,
then back home again
to play with you at being Robin Hood;
and when the shadows creep
round about, we can go
very quietly to sleep,
Babes in the Wood.

Leonard Clark

WEDDING DAY

Lillian McEever is bride for the day
Wearing Mummy's old wedding dress long locked away
And a posy of dandelions for her bouquet
And a tiara of daisies.

Birdsong showers silver on Institute Drive
Where Lillian waits for her guests to arrive
And the shouts and the laughter shake the morning alive
There's a wedding today.

Past the brook they wind where the cherry trees bloom
Casting white showers of blossom over bride and groom
And grandmothers dream in curtained front rooms
And remember.

Lillian McEever forget not this day
For Spring mornings die but memories stay
When the past like the dress is long locked away
And the leaves fall.

Gareth Owen

Little Maiden, better tarry;
Time enough next year to marry.
   Hearts may change,
   And so may fancy;
Wait a little longer, Nancy.

Anon

THE HAT

I love my beautiful hat more than anything
And through my beautiful hat I see a wedding ring
The King will marry me and make me his own before all
And when I am married I shall wear my hat and walk on the
      palace wall.

Stevie Smith

JEPHSON GARDENS

Two small children in the Gardens on Sunday,
Playing quietly at husband and wife.

How sweet, says an old lady, as she sits on
The bench: you must surely be brother and sister?

No, says the boy, we are husband and wife.
How sweet, says the old lady: but really you are
Brother and sister, aren't you now, really?

No, says the boy, trapped in his fantasy,
I am the husband, she is the wife.

The old lady moves off, she doesn't like liars,
She says. She doesn't think we are sweet any longer.

D. J. Enright

4 · *Childhood's flickering shadow*

The place felt cool and dark, and the motion of the swing seemed to set the breeze blowing. It waved Katy's hair like a great fan, and made her dreamy and quiet. All sorts of sleepy ideas began to flit through her brain. Swinging to and fro like the pendulum of a great clock, she gradually rose higher and higher, driving herself along by the motion of her body, and striking the floor smartly with her foot, at every sweep. Now she was at the top of the high arched door. Then she could almost touch the cross-beam above it, and through the small square window could see pigeons sitting and pluming themselves on the eaves of the barn, and white clouds blowing over the blue sky. She had never swung so high before. It was like flying, she thought, and she bent and curved more strongly in the seat, trying to send herself yet higher, and graze the roof with her toes.

Susan Coolidge: WHAT KATY DID

The dreaded hour would chime, the inevitable begging for ten minutes' grace would as inevitably be dismissed, and the grisly business of the night begin. The house was a tall one and nearly to the top of it I must climb. The lower flights of stairs were grey in a kind of floating twilight, for on the second landing a tiny jet of gas, turned economically down to not much more than a blue spark, shone feebly and revealed a door open – always slightly open – which I must pass on my way up. Beyond that door was a shadowy room, in which, only too apparent, stood a wardrobe whose dark polished doors were like huge condor wings, flapping "invisible woe". Of that wardrobe I was terrified. How often had I seen its doors open stealthily (and oh! so slowly), while the pale waxy fingers of a dead hand just appeared between them.

Forrest Reid: APOSTATE

EVENING IN THE PARK

Straight to the seesaw we both run,
Jenny and I;
Myself a boy so solitary—
Jenny so shy.

She does not say, 'The seesaw! Look!
Let's take it, Don!'
But runs when I do, holds one end,
And clambers on.

Quickly we gather speed—now low,
Now high in air;
It seems a so unlooked-for thing
To see her there—

See Jenny in her light blue dress,
Legs firm astride,
Both hands grasping the iron bar,
Eyes darkly wide.

The evening air is warm: a breath,
Dry and sweet-sour,
Blows from the kicked dust and from
The elder-flower.

Fragrant and warm and dusty-dry
The soft air blows.
One moment we spring lightly up—
Then down on toes

That tip the ground, no more...
                    The day
Leans towards dark;
By twos and threes the children move
Across the park.

Now in the elder-twig no bird
Is left to sing;
The last voice fades, and fades the distant
Churn of a swing.

Yet still beneath this waning light
With dreamful zest
We rise and fall; till, tired at last,
We sink to rest.

For a minute more we stay so,
Jenny and I;
Then down she slips, and runs off home
With no good-bye.

John Walsh

THE SWING

The garden-swing at the lawn's edge
Is hung beneath the hawthorn-hedge;
White branches droop above, and shed
Their petals on the swinger's head.
Here, now the day is almost done,
And leaves are pierced by the last sun,
I sit where hawthorn-breezes creep
Round me, and swing the hours to sleep:
Swinging alone –
By myself alone –
Alone,
Alone,
Alone.

In a soft shower the hawthorn-flakes descend.
Dusk falls at last. The dark-leaved branches bend
Earthward... The longest dream must have an end.

Now in my bedroom half-undressed,
My face against the window pressed,
I see once more the things which day
Gave me, and darkness takes away:
The garden-path still dimly white,
The lawn, the flower-beds sunk in night,
And, brushed by some uncertain breeze,
A ghostly swing beneath ghostly trees:
Swinging alone –
By itself alone –
Alone,
Alone,
Alone.

John Walsh

A SMALL GIRL SWINGING

When first they pushed me
  I was very scared.
My tummy jiggled. I was
  Unprepared.

The second time was higher
  And my ears
Were cold with whisperings
  Of tiny fears.

The third time up was HIGH,
  My teeth on edge.
My heart leapt off the bedroom
  Windowledge.

The fourth time, Oh, the fourth time
  It was mad.
My skirt flew off the world
  And I was glad.

No one's pushing now,
  My ears are ringing.
Who'll see across the park
  A small girl swinging?

Who'll hear across the park
  Her mother calling,
And everywhere her shadows
  Rising, falling?

George Szirtes

SHADOWS

Are they shadows that we see?
  And can shadows pleasure give?
Pleasures only shadows be,
  Cast by bodies we conceive,
  And are made the things we deem
  In those figures which they seem.

But these pleasures vanish fast,
  Which by shadows are expressed;
Pleasures are not, if they last;
  In their passing is their best.
  Glory is most bright and gay
  In a flash and so away.

Feed apace, then, greedy eyes
  On the wonder you behold;
Take it sudden as it flies,
  Though you take it not to hold.
  When your eyes have done their part,
  Thought must length it in the heart.

                              Tethys' Festival, 1610

Samuel Daniel

    Follow a shadow, it still flies you,
    Seem to fly it, it will pursue...

    Ben Jonson

NURSE'S SONG

When the voices of children are heard on the green,
　　And laughing is heard on the hill,
My heart is at rest within my breast,
　　And everything else is still.

'Then come home, my children, the sun is gone down,
　　And the dews of night arise;
Come, come, leave off play, and let us away
　　Till the morning appears in the skies.'

'No, no, let us play, for it is yet day,
　　And we cannot go to sleep;
Besides, in the sky the little birds fly,
　　And the hills are all cover'd with sheep.'

'Well, well, go and play till the light fades away,
　　And then go home to bed.'
The little ones leapèd and shouted and laugh'd
　　And all the hills echoèd.

William Blake

VILLAGE BEFORE SUNSET

There is a moment country children know
When half across the field the shadows go
And even the birds sing leisurely and slow.

There's timelessness in every passing tread;
Even the far-off train as it puffs ahead,
Even the voices calling them to bed.

Frances Cornford

GOING TO BED

'It is time to go to bed?'
Oh! how soon the words are spoken,
Oh! how sweet a spell is broken
When those words of fate are said
    'It is time to go to bed!'
    'Is it time to go to bed?'
Surely bed awhile can wait
    Till the pleasant tale is read
  At our father's knee; how cheery
  Burns the fire! We are not weary,
    Why should it be time for bed,
Just because the clock strikes eight?
While they talk, let us be hiding
  Just behind the great arm-chairs;
It may be they will forget us,
It may be that they will let us
  Stay to supper, stay to prayers;
  Go at last with them upstairs,
  Hand in hand with Father, Mother;
    Kisses given and good-nights said,
'Twill be time for Sister, Brother,
    Time for me to go to bed!

Dora Greenwell

NIGHT THOUGHT

Oh, what's the good of staying up and yawning
And using up the artificial light?
For anything may happen in the morning,
And nothing ever happens in the night.

E. V. Rieu

EARLY SUPPER

Laughter of children brings
  The kitchen down with laughter.
While the old kettle sings
Laughter of children brings
To a boil all savoury things.
  Higher than beam or rafter,
Laughter of children brings
  The kitchen down with laughter.

So ends an autumn day,
  Light ripples on the ceiling,
Dishes are stacked away;
So ends an autumn day,
The children jog and sway
  In comic dances wheeling.
So ends an autumn day,
  Light ripples on the ceiling.

They trail upstairs to bed,
  And night is a dark tower.
The kettle calls: instead
They trail upstairs to bed,
Leaving warmth, the coppery-red
  Mood of their carnival hour.
They trail upstairs to bed,
  And night is a dark tower.

Barbara Howes

A CHILD UPON THE STAIR

Now when I stand upon the stair alone
   And listen, I can hear a quiet stir
Like even breathing, or a whispered drone,
   A sound that any little noise would blur.
I know that there is something in this hall,
   That climbs the waiting stairs and then goes down
On silent feet, or clings hard to the wall,
   As though it loved the old and faded brown.
Sometimes I feel that I, myself, can fly
   If I stand very still upon the stair,
Believing that there is no reason why
   I cannot trust my body to the air...
Do other children find their stairs so near
   To things that grown-ups say cannot be here?

Carolyn Hall

Matthew, Mark, Luke and John,
Bless the bed that I lie on.
Four corners to my bed,
Four angels round my head.
One to watch and one to pray
And two to bear my soul away.

Anon

R. FALLING OUT OF BED

That's how fooling often ends, you see —
giggling and talking after you'd been sent
to bed, fooling about
and falling out.

Oh but you're not hurt. I'm
only cross because I feared a broken bone.
Now settle down and sleep.

When the house is quiet again I
suddenly realise what flashed into my mind
hearing that tumble upstairs, that
bony bundling on the floor — the moment
of birth, the extraordinary sensation
of the limbs being thrust from my body
bundling smoothly out like the knobbed
rolling of apples in a sack and I almost
identifying then, in that excited moment,
the pointed chin, the symmetry of ribs, frail
elbows, knees, all tumbling into unexpected life.

Molly Holden

NOTHING
(for Ruth)

Her sixth midsummer eve keeps Ruth awake.
The silent house is full of yellow light—
Put out, from time to time, by prowling clouds;
The dripping tap, an unsuspected heart
Somewhere inside the house, seems to grow louder;
Street noises have an unfamiliar ring.
She cannot shut her ears, but even her eyelids
Let through the silent play of light and shade.

At last she leaves her bed and creeps downstairs,
Trembling a little; whispers 'I'm afraid.'
'Afraid of what'? 'Of nothing.' When we laugh,
Saying 'That means you're not afraid,' she cries,
And says, more loudly, 'I'm afraid of Nothing';
Says it again, till suddenly we see it—
Nothing outside the windows; Nothing after
The longest day; Nothing inside the house;
Nothing where everything seemed set for ever.

Edward Lowbury

HERE WE GO ROUND THE MULBERRY BUSH

There is a bush that no one sees,
The loveliest of little trees.
Full of sweet dark mulberries.

Round and round it children go,
Sometimes quick and sometimes slow,
Singing words all children know.

While they sing the bush is there
Planted in the empty air,
With fruit for every child to share,

Little girls with sandalled foot,
Little boys in clumping boot,
Running round the mulberry root,

Fair and dark ones, loitering, leaping,
Gay and grave ones, laughing, weeping,
Playing, working, waking, sleeping.

When the moment's game is done,
When the playing child is gone,
The unseen mulberry bush stands on,

And with all its leafy eyes
Childhood's flickering shadow spies
Dancing down the centuries,

And with all its leafy ears
Evermore the footstep hears
Of vanished childhood's hundred years,

Singing still without a sound,
Running silently around
The bush that never grew in ground.

Eleanor Farjeon

AND SO TO BED

'Night-night, my Precious!'; 'Sweet dreams, Sweet!'
'Heaven bless you, Child!' – the accustomed grown-ups said.
Two eyes gazed mutely back that none could meet,
Then turned to face Night's terrors overhead.

Walter de la Mare

SHADOW MARCH

All round the house is the jet-black night;
  It stares through the window-pane;
It crawls in the corners, hiding from the light,
  And it moves with the moving flame.

Now my little heart goes a-beating like a drum,
  With the breath of the Bogie in my hair;
And all round the candle the crooked shadows come
  And go marching along up the stair.

The shadow of the balusters, the shadow of the lamp,
  The shadow of the child that goes to bed –
All the wicked shadows coming, tramp, tramp, tramp,
  With the black night overhead.

Robert Louis Stevenson

INTIMATIONS OF MORTALITY

The shadows of the banisters march march,
The lovers linger under the arch,
On the beach the waves creep,
The little boy cannot go to sleep.

He is afraid of God and the Devil—
If he shuts his eyes they will draw level,
So he watches the half-open door and waits
For people on the stairs carrying lights.

Someone comes, carrying a lamp,
The shadows of the banisters march march,
All is above board, order is restored,
Time on horseback under a Roman arch.

Then the final darkness for eight hours
The murderous grin of toothy flowers,
The tick of his pulse in the pillow, the sick
Vertigo of falling in a fanged pit.

After one perfunctory kiss
His parents snore in conjugal bliss.
The night watchman with crossed thumbs
Grows an idol. The Kingdom comes...

Louis Macneice

IN THE NIGHT

Out of my window late at night I gape
And see the stars but do not watch them really,
And hear the trains but do not listen clearly;
Inside my mind I turn about to keep
Myself awake, yet am not there entirely.
Something of me is out in the dark landscape.

How much am I then what I think, how much what I feel?
How much the eye that seems to keep stars straight?
Do I control what I can contemplate
Or is it my vision that's amenable?
I turn in my mind, my mind is a room whose wall
I can see the top of but never completely scale.

All that I love is, like the night, outside,
Good to be gazed at, looking as if it could
With a simple gesture be brought inside my head
Or in my heart. But my thoughts about it divide
Me from my object. Now deep in my bed
I turn and the world turns on the other side.

Elizabeth Jennings

Here we are all, by day; by night we are hurled
By dreams, each one into a several world.

Robert Herrick

TO SLEEP

O soft embalmer of the still midnight!
Shutting, with careful fingers and benign,
Our gloom-pleased eyes, embowered from the light,
Enshaded in forgetfulness divine:
O soothest Sleep! if so it please thee, close,
In midst of this mine hymn, my willing eyes,
Or wait the amen, ere thy poppy throws
Around my head its lulling charities;
Then save me, or the passed day will shine
Upon my pillow, breeding many woes;
Save me from curious conscience, that still lords
Its strength, for darkness burrowing like a mole:
Turn the key deftly in the oiled wards,
And seal the hushed casket of my soul.

John Keats

THE NIGHT WILL NEVER STAY

The night will never stay,
The night will still go by,
Though with a million stars
You pin it to the sky;
Though you bind it with the blowing wind
And buckle it with the moon,
The night will slip away
Like sorrow or a tune.

Eleanor Farjeon

THE EARLY MORNING

The moon on the one hand, the dawn on the other:
The moon is my sister, the dawn is my brother.
The moon on my left and the dawn on my right.
My brother, good morning: my sister, goodnight.

Hilaire Belloc

THE WAKING

I wake to sleep, and take my waking slow.
I feel my fate in what I cannot fear.
I learn by going where I have to go.

We think by feeling. What is there to know?
I hear my being dance from ear to ear.
I wake to sleep, and take my waking slow.

Of those so close beside me, which are you?
God bless the Ground! I shall walk softly there,
And learn by going where I have to go.

Light takes the Tree; but who can tell us how?
The lowly worm climbs up a winding stair;
I wake to sleep, and take my waking slow.

Great Nature has another thing to do
To you and me; so take the lively air,
And, lovely, learn by going where to go.

This shaking keeps me steady. I should know.
What falls away is always. And is near.
I wake to sleep, and take my waking slow.
I learn by going where I have to go.

Theodore Roethke

GOD'S GRANDEUR

The world is charged with the grandeur of God.
  It will flame out, like shining from shook foil;
  It gathers to a greatness, like the ooze of oil
Crushed. Why do men then now not reck his rod?
Generations have trod, have trod, have trod;
  And all is seared with trade; bleared, smeared with toil;
  And wears man's smudge and shares man's smell: the soil
Is bare now, nor can foot feel, being shod.

And for all this, nature is never spent;
  There lives the dearest freshness deep down things;
And though the last lights off the black West went
  Oh, morning, at the brown brink eastward, springs—
Because the Holy Ghost over the bent
  World broods with warm breast and with ah! bright wings.

Gerard Manley Hopkins

5 · *If I could tell you*

Writing and arithmetic were another matter. Writing was a joy! Vivid in one's mind as one licked the pencil and prepared for action the letters glowed, gaily coloured. Slender crimson-lake A; rotund, grass-green B; curving, beautiful smoke-blue C...I think these colours may have been imprinted on my mind by the square, brick-like blocks from which, at three years old, I had learnt the Alphabet with no trouble at all. For example 'A for apple' and there, on each of the four sides of the shiny white-surfaced block was depicted a big red Capital A; a small red a; and between each a large, ruddy apple. Even today, for me the initial letter of a word colours, so to speak, the whole...Architect, Aniseed; Academy...all are a rather watered-down mixture of vermilion and crimson lake.

Eve Garnett: FIRST AFFECTIONS

I remember the morning when Miss Spence opened my eyes to the life of words...what stories she read to us as we sat at her feet I don't remember, but suddenly words were not only sentences but individuals. She gave each word so exactly its proper weight and meaning, yet so lightly, I felt I could hold the words like coloured stones in my hand. Perhaps because my ears were alerted so were my eyes. I can still see the light touching the golden wood of the polished floorboards where we were sitting.

Christopher Fry: CAN YOU FIND ME?

THE CHILD IN THE ORCHARD

'He rolls in the orchard: he is stained with moss
And with earth, the solitary old white horse.
Where is his father and where is his mother
Among all the brown horses? Has he a brother?
I know the swallow, the hawk, and the hern;
But there are two million things for me to learn.

'Who was the lady that rode the white horse
With rings and bells to Banbury Cross?
Was there no other lady in England beside
That a nursery rhyme could take for a ride?
The swift, the swallow, the hawk, and the hern.
There are two million things for me to learn.

'Was there a man once who straddled across
The back of the Westbury White Horse
Over there on Salisbury Plain's green wall?
Was he bound for Westbury, or had he a fall?
The swift, the swallow, the hawk, and the hern.
There are two million things for me to learn.

'Out of all the white horses I know three,
At the age of six; and it seems to me
There is so much to learn, for men,
That I dare not go to bed again.
The swift, the swallow, the hawk, and the hern.
There are millions of things for me to learn.'

Edward Thomas

HOW MANY?

How many seconds in a minute?
Sixty, and no more in it.

How many minutes in an hour?
Sixty for sun and shower.

How many hours in a day?
Twenty-four for work and play.

How many days in a week?
Seven both to hear and speak.

How many weeks in a month?
Four, as the swift moon runn'th.

How many months in a year?
Twelve the almanack makes clear.

How many years in an age?
One hundred says the sage.

How many ages in time?
No one knows the rhyme.

Christina Rossetti

TIME, YOU OLD GIPSY MAN

Time, you old gipsy man,
  Will you not stay,
Put up your caravan
  Just for one day?
All things I'll give you
Will you be my guest,
Bells for your jennet
Of silver the best,
Goldsmiths shall beat you
A great golden ring,
Peacocks shall bow to you,
Little boys sing,
Oh, and sweet girls will
Festoon you with may,
Time, you old gipsy,
Why hasten away?

Last week in Babylon,
Last night in Rome,
Morning, and in the crush
Under Paul's dome;
Under Paul's dial
You tighten your rein—
Only a moment,
And off once again;
Off to some city
Now blind in the womb,
Off to another
Ere that's in the tomb.
  Time, you old gipsy man,
  Will you not stay,
Put up your caravan
  Just for one day?

Ralph Hodgson

IF I COULD TELL YOU

Time will say nothing but I told you so,
Time only knows the price we have to pay;
If I could tell you I would let you know.

If we should weep when clowns put on their show,
If we should stumble when musicians play,
Time will say nothing but I told you so.

There are no fortunes to be told, although,
Because I love you more than I can say,
If I could tell you I would let you know.

The winds must come from somewhere when they blow,
There must be reasons why the leaves decay;
Time will say nothing but I told you so.

Perhaps the roses really want to grow,
The vision seriously intends to stay;
If I could tell you I would let you know.

Suppose the lions all get up and go,
And all the brooks and soldiers run away;
Will Time say nothing but I told you so?
If I could tell you I would let you know.

W. H. Auden

WHO HAS SEEN THE WIND?

Who has seen the wind?
  Neither I nor you:
But when the leaves hang trembling
  The wind is passing thro'.

Who has seen the wind?
  Neither you nor I:
But when the trees bow down their heads
  The wind is passing by.

Christina Rossetti

SOUNDS

THE clock!
A crowing cock!
  And under these
  The murmur of the wind among the trees,
  The hum of bees.

The clock is busy Man with Time at strife,
Wasting brief hours to measure out his life!
The cock vainglorious Man chanting his praise,
Forgetful of the time—how short the days!

The wind is Man, dreaming and dreaming still,
Silence with music evermore to fill.
The bee is Man that neither hastes nor shirks,
Not happy and unhappy as he works.

Mary Coleridge

from ODE ON THE INTIMATIONS OF IMMORTALITY

There was a time when meadow, grove, and stream,
The earth, and every common sight,
      To me did seem
      Apparelled in celestial light,
The glory and the freshness of a dream.
It is not now as it has been of yore;—
      Turn wheresoe'er I may,
      By night or day,
The things which I have seen I now can see no more.

      The rainbow comes and goes,
      And lovely is the rose,
  The moon doth with delight
Look round her when the heavens are bare;
      Waters on a starry night
      Are beautiful and fair;
  The sunshine is a glorious birth;
  But yet I know, where'er I go,
That there hath passed away a glory from the earth.

Our birth is but a sleep and a forgetting:
The Soul that rises with us, our life's Star,
      Hath had elsewhere its setting,
      And cometh from afar:
      Not in entire forgetfulness,
      And not in utter nakedness,
But trailing clouds of glory do we come
      From God, who is our home:
Heaven lies about us in our infancy!
Shades of the prison-house begin to close
      Upon the growing Boy,
But He beholds the light, and whence it flows,

He sees it in his joy;
The Youth, who daily farther from the East
    Must travel, still is Nature's Priest,
        And by the vision splendid
        Is on his way attended;
At length the Man perceives it die away,
And fade into the light of common day.

William Wordsworth

SONG

Who can say
Why Today
Tomorrow will be yesterday?
Who can tell
Why to smell
The violet, recalls the dewy prime
Of youth and buried time?
The cause is nowhere found in rhyme.

Alfred Lord Tennyson

from CHILDHOOD

The past it is a magie word
Too beautiful to last
It looks back like a lovely face
Who can forget the past
There's music in its childhood
That's known in every tongue
Like the music of the wildwood
All chorus to the song

The happy dream the joyous play
The life without a sigh
The beauty thoughts can ne'er portray
In those four letters lye
The painters' beauty breathing arts
The poets' speaking pens
Can ne'er call back a thousand part
Of what that word contains...

The morn when first we went to school
Who can forget the morn
When the birchwhip lay upon the clock
& our hornbook it was torn
We tore the little pictures out
Less fond of books than play
& only took one letter home
& that the letter 'A'...

John Clare

ALPHABETS

A shadow his father makes with joined hands
And thumbs and fingers nibbles on the wall
Like a rabbit's head. He understands
He will understand more when he goes to school.

There he draws smoke with chalk the whole first week,
Then draws the forked stick that they call a Y.
This is writing. A swan's neck and swan's back
Make the 2 he can see now as well as say.

Two rafters and a cross-tie on the slate
Are the letter some call *ah*, some call *ay*.
There are charts, there are headlines, there is a right
Way to hold the pen and a wrong way.

First it is 'copying out', and then 'English'
Marked correct with a little leaning hoe.
Smells of inkwells rise in the classroom hush.
A globe in the window tilts like a coloured O.

Seamus Heaney

Great A, little a, bouncing B,
The cat's in the cupboard and she can't see me.

Traditional

FIRST DAY AT SCHOOL

A millionbillionwillion miles from home
Waiting for the bell to go. (To go where?)
Why are they all so big, other children?
So noisy? So much at home they
must have been born in uniform.
Lived all their lives in playgrounds.
Spent the years inventing games
that don't let me in. Games
that are rough, that swallow you up.

And the railings.
All around, the railings.
Are they to keep out wolves and monsters?
Things that carry off and eat children?
Things you don't take sweets from?
Perhaps they're to stop us getting out.
Running away from the lessins. Lessin.
What does a lessin look like?
Sounds small and slimy.
They keep them in glassrooms.
Whole rooms made out of glass. Imagine.

I wish I could remember my name.
Mummy said it would come in useful.
Like wellies. When there's puddles.
Yellowwellies. I wish she was here.
I think my name is sewn on somewhere.
Perhaps the teacher will read it for me.
Tea-cher. The one who makes the tea.

Roger McGough

ISN'T MY NAME MAGICAL?

Nobody can see my name on me.
My name is inside
and all over me, unseen
like other people also keep it.
Isn't my name magical?

My name is mine only.
It tells I am individual,
the one special person it shakes
when I'm wanted.

Even if someone else answers
for me, my message hangs in air
haunting others, till it stops
with me, the right name.
Isn't your name and my name magic?

If I'm with hundreds of people
and my name gets called,
my sound switches me on to answer
like it was my human electricity.

My name echoes across playground,
it comes, it demands my attention.
I have to find out who calls,
who wants me for what.
My name gets blurted out in class,
it is terror, at a bad time,
because somebody is cross.

My name gets called in a whisper
I am happy, because
my name may have touched me
with a loving voice.
Isn't your name and my name magic?

James Berry

A LITTLE MISTAKE

I studied my tables over and over, and backward and forward, too;
But I couldn't remember six times nine, and I didn't know what
    to do,
Till sister told me to play with my doll, and not to bother my
    head.
'If you call her "Fifty-four" for a while, you'll learn it by heart,'
    she said.

So I took my favourite Mary Ann (though I thought 'twas a
    dreadful shame
To give such a perfectly lovely child such a perfectly horrid name),
And I called her my dear little 'Fifty-four' a hundred times, till
    I knew
The answer of six times nine as well as the answer of two times
    two.

Next day, Elizabeth Wigglesworth, who always seems so proud,
Said, 'Six times nine is fifty-two,' and I nearly laughed aloud!
But I wished I hadn't when teacher said, 'Now, Dorothy, tell if
    you can,'
For I thought of my doll, and — oh dear me! — I answered
    'Mary Ann!'

Anna M. Pratt

FIRST DAY
(for Moelwyn Merchant)

Myope, jackdaw-tongued, I was fetched to school
Too early. ('Only child. Needs company.')
School was an ark of slate and granite, beached
Between the allotments and the castle ditch.

Cased on the roof, the famous Hanging Bell:
Came, 1840, from the county gaol.
I'm 1917, from Old Hill, rigged out
In regulation infant gear: knitted

Green jersey, cords snagging both knees, new boots
With tags that locked my feet together. Hold
The tin mug with my cocoa money in.
A washed September morning, and the gas

Was on. Over the teacher's desk I saw
A cross made out of wood. Small steps led up,
But nobody was on it. Miss Treglown
Was writing down my name in a big book.

'Where's Jesus?' Without lifting up her head,
'Jesus is everywhere,' Miss Treglown said.
As if on cue, trapped in its rusted tower,
The Hanging Bell came to. Banged out the hour.

Charles Causley

PAINT BOX

He tried to tell them what he felt,
could say it only in colours –
Sunday's white page shading to grey
of evening clocks and bells-in-the-rain.
Monday morning, bright yellow brass
of a cock crowing.
Story-time, purple.
Scarlet is shouting in the playground.

His world's a cocoon
round as an egg, an acorn
sprouting green.
The schoolroom square and hard,
his desk hard and square
facing the enemy blackboard.

'You must learn to read,' they said
and gave him a painting-book alphabet.
Apple swelled beautifully red. Balloon
expanded in blue.
C was a cage for a bird;
his brush wavered through
painting himself
a small brown smudge inside.

Phoebe Hesketh

WALKING AWAY
(for Sean)

It is eighteen years ago, almost to the day –
A sunny day with the leaves just turning,
The touch-lines new-ruled – since I watched you play
Your first game of football, then, like a satellite
Wrenched from its orbit, go drifting away

Behind a scatter of boys. I can see
You walking away from me towards the school
With the pathos of a half-fledged thing set free
Into a wilderness, the gait of one
Who finds no path where the path should be.

That hesitant figure, eddying away
Like a winged seed loosened from its parent stem,
Has something I never quite grasp to convey
About nature's give-and-take – the small, the scorching
Ordeals which fire one's irresolute clay.

I have had worse partings, but none that so
Gnaws at my mind still. Perhaps it is roughly
Saying what God alone could perfectly show –
How selfhood begins with a walking away,
And love is proved in the letting go.

C. Day Lewis

HALF-PAST TWO

Once upon a schooltime
He did Something Very Wrong
(I forget what it was).

And She said he'd done
Something Very Wrong, and must
Stay in the school-room till half-past two.

(Being cross, she'd forgotten
She hadn't taught him Time.
He was too scared at being wicked to remind her.)

He knew a lot of time: he knew
Gettinguptime, timeyouwereofftime,
Timetogohomenowtime, TVtime,

Timeformykisstime (that was Grantime).
All the important times he knew,
But not half-past two.

He knew the clockface, the little eyes
And two long legs for walking,
But he couldn't click its language,

So he waited, beyond onceupona,
Out of reach of all the timefors,
And knew he'd escaped for ever

Into the smell of old chrysanthemums on Her desk,
Into the silent noise his hangnail made,
Into the air outside the window, into ever.

And then, *My goodness*, she said,
Scuttling in, *I forgot all about you.*
Run along or you'll be late.

So she slotted him back into schooltime,
And he got home in time for teatime,
Nexttime, notimeforthatnowtime,

But he never forgot how once by not knowing time,
He escaped into the lockless land of ever,
Where time hides tick-less waiting to be born.

U.A. Fanthorpe

TWO BAD THINGS IN INFANT SCHOOL

Learning bad grammar, then getting blamed for it:
Learning Our Father which art in Heaven.

Bowing our heads to a hurried nurse, and
Hearing the nits rattle down on the paper.

AND TWO GOOD THINGS

Listening to Miss Anthony, our lovely Miss,
Charming us dumb with *The Wind in the Willows*.

Dancing Sellinger's Round, and dancing and
Dancing it, and getting it perfect forever.

D. J. Enright

YOU LEARNING TO READ

Weeks and weeks of
'How do you spell car?
C–C–Car is like Cat
Cat is like Mat
Mat is like Cat said the bells of Saint Fat!'
– a wild dash through
islands of syllables,
tributaries of sound, a whole
spinning world of rhyme –
'World is like Curled said the bells of Saint Burld!'
Then 'Teach me to read. Get me a book to read'.
And the first book – charmless, chanting
This is a This is a This is a
with huge raw drawings colouring the noun.
In five minutes you were tired, alarmed –
it was so hard, so perfectly immovable.
There was no escape. You got it or you didn't.
And when you failed, reading
'This is a dog' instead
of 'Here is a shop' it was
a chasm to cry into.
But bouncing again into our bed next morning, shouting
'I can read said Mr Bead' you splodged
words with a finger, frowning to recall
the right sound. And it slowly came.
Objects to touch and taste grew into words.
Soon you were pointing them out in the street,
triumphant, shouting the letters. Then
came the verbs, then the first small abstracts –
the right sound became the right word became the right thing
and all the world's now spellable
except
except

your own secrets that no book will spell
or colour crudely, or outline safe in black.
It never stops – that name-read-spell
game, and gets no easier. It can turn out well,
just keep that bounce up, keep up that attack.

Brian Jones

WORDS AND MONSTERS

When he was eight years old he had become
Hungry for words, and he would munch his way
Through comics, adverts, anything with some
Printed food to hold the pangs at bay.
His friends would hoard up birds' eggs, shells or stamps,
But he collected words. One day he saw –
As he walked lonely down the town's main street –
A poster done in thunderous colours, raw
And red as flesh of newly butchered meat:
A picture of a lady, mouth distressed,
Eyes wild and fat with fear; and, underneath,
These glaring words: *THE ABYSMAL BRUTE – The Best
Movie of the Year*. He felt his teeth
Bite on the word *abysmal* as you test
The goodness of a coin. This one was fine.
He took it home to add it to the rest
Of his collection. He liked its shape and shine
But did not know its worth. Inside his head
Its echo rang. He asked his mother what
Abysmal meant. 'Bottomless,' she said.

The Abysmal Brute was grunting in the hot
Dark outside, would follow him to bed.

Vernon Scannell

TO LALLA, READING MY VERSES
TOPSY-TURVY

Darling little Cousin,
  With your thoughtful look
Reading topsy-turvy
  From a printed book

English hieroglyphics,
  More mysterious
To you, than Egyptian
  Ones would be to us;—

Leave off for a minute
  Studying, and say
What is the impression
  That those marks convey?

Only solemn silence,
  And a wondering smile:
But your eyes are lifted
  Unto mine the while.

In their gaze so steady
  I can surely trace
That a happy spirit
  Lighteth up your face.

Tender, happy spirit,
  Innocent and pure;
Teaching more than science,
  And than learning more.

How should I give answer
  To that asking look?
Darling little Cousin
  Go back to your book.
Read on: if you knew it,
  You have cause to boast:—
You are much the wisest,
  Though I know the most.

Christina Rossetti

6 · *Tread softly here*

At the top of one of the streets parallel to ours, but at that time divided from it by that big private meadow with the pond and elm-trees, I stopped and looked down. For there lived Mabel Looms, a schoolfellow whom I adored. She had had a Christmas card from me that morning. The street was empty. I walked backwards and forwards along the Grove past the top of the street, waiting, sufficiently proud not to be overcome by long disappointment. At last Mabel came up towards the Common, in the company of some elders. Without a sign I continued walking backwards and forwards. They turned to their left at the top, away from our street. I turned in the opposite direction homeward, pleased with my swinging sword and believing that the passers-by admired it. At home they knew well where I had been. My attachment to Mabel lasted for several years and more than once after it had been broken I attempted to renew it. She was a perfect loving friend. I thought her beautiful.

Edward Thomas: THE CHILDHOOD OF EDWARD THOMAS

MOON PENNY

Moon penny
   bright as silver
Come and play with
   little children.

Anon

FULL MOON AND LITTLE FRIEDA

A cool small evening shrunk to a dog bark and the clank of a bucket—

And you listening.
A spider's web, tense for the dew's touch.
A pail lifted, still and brimming—mirror
To tempt a first star to a tremor.

Cows are going home in the lane there, looping the hedges with their
     warm wreaths of breath—
A dark river of blood, many boulders,
Balancing unspilled milk.

'Moon!' you cry suddenly, 'Moon! Moon!'

The moon has stepped back like an artist gazing amazed at a work
That points at him amazed.

Ted Hughes

BROKEN MOON
(for Emma)

Twelve, small as six,
strength, movement, hearing
all given in half measure,
my daughter,
child of genetic carelessness,
walks uphill, always.

I watch her morning face;
precocious patience as she hooks each sock,
creeps it up her foot,
aims her jersey like a quoit.
My fingers twitch;
her private frown deters.

Her jokes can sting:
'My life is like dressed crab
—lot of effort, rather little meat.'
Yet she delights in seedlings taking root,
finding a fossil,
a surprise dessert.

Chopin will not yield to her stiff touch;
I hear her cursing.
She paces Bach exactly,
firm rounding of perfect cadences.
Somewhere inside
she is dancing a courante.

In dreams she skims the sand,
curls toes into the ooze of pools,
leaps on to stanchions.

Awake, her cousins take her hands;
they lean into the waves,
stick–child between curved sturdiness.

She turns away from stares,
laughs at the boy who asks
if she will find a midget husband.
Ten years ago, cradling her,
I showed her the slice of silver in the sky.
'Moon broken,' she said.

Carole Satyamurti

UNIFORM

'You'll grow,' she said and that was that. No use
To argue and to sulk invited slaps.
The empty shoulders drooped, the sleeves hung loose –
No use – she nods and the assistant wraps.

New blazer, new school socks and all between
Designed for pea pod anonymity.
All underwear the regulation green;
Alike there's none to envy, none to pity.

At home she feasts on pins. She tacks and tucks
Takes in the generous seams and smiles at thrift.
I fidget as she fits. She tuts and clucks.
With each neat stitch she digs a deeper rift.

They'll mock me with her turnings and her hem
And laugh and know that I'm not one of them.

Jan Dean

FIREFLY SONG

Firefly in the pool of water,
Bring me up a little silver,
Bring me up a star for the delight of it,
Bring me up a broken moon.

Firefly, firefly, in the water,
Bring me up a golden river,
Bring me up a fish with a light on it,
Bring me up a crooked moon.

Elizabeth Madox Roberts

MY PARENTS

My parents kept me from children who were rough
Who threw words like stones and wore torn clothes
Their thighs showed through rags they ran in the street
And climbed cliffs and stripped by the country streams.

I feared more than tigers their muscles like iron
Their jerking hands and their knees tight on my arms
I feared the salt coarse pointing of those boys
Who copied my lisp behind me on the road.

They were lithe they sprang out behind hedges
Like dogs to bark at my world. They threw mud
While I looked the other way, pretending to smile.
I longed to forgive them but they never smiled.

Stephen Spender

'FALSE FRIENDS — LIKE'

When I was still a boy and mother's pride,
A bigger boy spoke up to me so kind — like,
'If you do like, I'll treat you with a ride
In this wheelbarrow.' So then I was blind — like
To what he had a-working in his mind — like
And mounted for a passenger inside;
And coming to a puddle — pretty wide,
He tipp'd me in, a-grinning back behind — like.
So when a man may come to me so thick — like,
And shake my hand where once he passed me by,
And tell me he would do me this or that,
I can't help thinking of the big boy's trick — like,
And then, for all I can but wag my hat,
And thank him, I do feel a little shy.

William Barnes

POEM

I loved my friend.
He went away from me.
There's nothing more to say.
The poem ends,
Soft as it began —
I loved my friend.

Langston Hughes

BIG HOLE

My best friend Jenny Colquhoun has moved on.
She's gone to live in a posher part of town.
She left a big hole; an empty space next to my desk.
My hands hold themselves on the way to school.

But see in her new house she has a dining room,
a TV room—imagine a room just for watching!—
and her own bedroom. I stayed the night;
got lost on my way back from the bathroom.

I was there the day before her ninth birthday.
I was the special friend from the old school.
But when her new friends came they stared
till I thought I should check the mirror, as if

I had a big hole in my tights. 'What did *you*
get Jenny for her birthday?' '*Anne of Green Gables*'
I said, burning under the wrong dress,
wanting the thick carpet to swallow me up.

'Have you always been that colour?' says the one
with the freckles. And a giggle spreads from room
to room till Jenny's beautiful red-haired mother
saves me: '*Anne of Green Gables*? A wonderful book.'

Jackie Kay

THE SMILE

It began with a whisper
But grew and grew
Until I felt certain
The source must be you.
Why did you smile
While I listened and then
Turn away as their faces
Fell silent again?

What had you told them
That slammed shut their looks
Like the end of a lesson
With unpopular books?
What was the writing
Which I couldn't see
As it hid between covers
And pointed at me?

Nothing much could have happened
For by the next day
We were laughing, talking,
And managed to stay
(Well, after a fashion)
Good friends for a while
But with always between us
The ghost of that smile.

John Mole

SAVING GRACE

Fish do not smile, nor birds: their faces are not
Equipped for it. A smiling dog's the illusion
And wish-fulfilment of its owner. Cats wear
Permanent smiles inspired by mere politeness.
But human animals at times forget their
Godlike responsibilities; the tension
Slackens, the weasel-sharp intentness falters;
Muscles relax; the eyes refrain from peering
Aside, before and after; and the burden
Of detail drops from forehead; cheekline gently
Creases; the mouth wide-flowers; the stiff mask softens;
And Man bestows his simple, unambitious,
Unservile, unselfseeking, undeceptive,
Uncorrupt gift, the grace-note of a smile.

A. S. J. Tessimond

They might not need me – yet they might –
I'll let my heart be just in sight –
A smile so small as mine might be
Precisely their necessity.

Emily Dickinson

OF PERFECT FRIENDSHIP

True friendship unfeignëd
Doth rest unrestrainëd,
   No terror can tame it:
Not gaining, nor losing,
Nor gallant gay glosing,
   Can ever reclaim it.
In pain, and in pleasure,
The most truest treasure
   That may be desirëd,
Is loyal love deemëd,
Of wisdom esteemëd
   And chiefly requirëd.

Anon (1579)

HE AND SHE

'SHOULD one of us remember,
   And one of us forget,
I wish I knew what each will do,
   But who can tell as yet?'

'Should one of us remember,
   And one of us forget,
I promise you what I will do —
And I'm content to wait for you,
   And not be sure as yet.'

Christina Rossetti

DOTTING THE I'S IN MISSISSIPPI

Don't turn round, Miss Fisher,

I want to watch the way you twirl the chalk,
when you write Mississippi,
dotting i's like currants in a cake.

When you reach for the ruler
my eyes grow warm and prickly—your arm
is whiter than the letters on the board.

I'm glad you liked my story
of the teacher rescued
by a stern-faced boy with glasses

from the seething swamp.
But why did you give the gold star
to Ginger Clay? He says

your eyes are slanting.
And anyway, in nature-study lesson,
he sent his broken tooth to Nancy Powell.

It was me that left the lettuce
by that soppy photo in your desk. I'm sorry
the caterpillar crawled into your glove.

When you stand by the window
the sunlight on your hair smells of bracken.
So I raise my desk-lid,

breathe on the butterfly
that rested on your blouse
when you took Class IV up Frodsham Hill.

Please turn round, Miss Fisher, don't speak.
Just let me watch you through this knot-hole.
I want to count the colours in your eyes.

John Latham

from SUMMONED BY BELLS

O Peggy Purey-Cust, how pure you were:
My first and purest love, Miss Purey-Cust!
Satchel on back I hurried up West Hill
To catch you on your morning walk to school,
Your nanny with you and your golden hair
Streaming like sunlight. Strict deportment made
You hold yourself erect and every step
Bounced up and down as though you walked on springs.
Your ice-blue eyes, your lashes long and light,
Your sweetly freckled face and turned-up nose
So haunted me that all my loves since then
Have had a look of Peggy Purey-Cust.
Along the Grove, what happy, happy steps
Under the limes I took to Byron House,
And blob-work, weaving, carpentry and art,
Walking with you; and with what joy returned.
Wendy you were to me in *Peter Pan*,
The Little Match Girl in Hans Andersen—
But I would rescue you before you died.
And once you asked me to your house to tea:
It seemed a palace after 31—
The lofty entrance hall, the flights of stairs,
The huge expanse of sunny drawing-room,
Looking for miles across the chimney-pots
To spired St Pancras and the dome of Paul's;
And there your mother from a sofa smiled.
After that tea I called and called again,
But Peggy was not in. She was away;
She wasn't well. *House of the Sleeping Winds*,
My favourite book with whirling art-nouveau
And Walter Crane-ish colour plates, I brought
To cheer her sick-bed. It was taken in.
Weeks passed and passed... and then it was returned.
Oh gone for ever, Peggy Purey-Cust!

John Betjeman

ROGER BAVIDGE

Not for his curly mop and freckled nose,
his concertina socks and scabby knees,
nor for his cleverness, but just because
he was my sort of person, I suppose,
I felt this tenderness, but could not name
my feeling at that time. I was too young,
    but Shakespeare could have named it,
    Shakespeare knew
    a thing or two of love.

And we were sitting talking, side by side
on the high vaulting-horse, when someone said
'Is Roger your fiancé?' I denied
that I had any feelings, though I had,
and afterwards disguised my tenderness
with scorn, like Beatrice insulting Ben
    five hundred years ago, for Shakespeare knew
    a thing or two of love.

I mocked his curly mop and freckled nose,
his concertina socks and scabby knees;
though I was scruffy too, I mocked his clothes.
We were ten or eleven, I suppose.
'Your socks are full of holes, your shirt is ripped;
why doesn't someone mend them?' Roger wept.
    Benedict could answer blow for blow,
    but Roger Bavidge, forty years ago,
    knew something even Shakespeare could not know.

Our teacher told me later: 'Roger cried
because, six months ago, his mother died.'
Never again did we sit side by side
discussing this and that. I should have tried

to make amends for being such a savage
to one who was my friend. Dear Roger Bavidge,
     do you remember me? And do you know
     what Shakespeare knew five hundred years ago?

Anna Adams

SONNET 98

From you have I been absent in the spring,
When proud-pied April, dress'd in all his trim,
Hath put a spirit of youth in every thing,
That heavy Saturn laugh'd and leap'd with him.
Yet nor the lays of birds, nor the sweet smell
Of different flowers in odour and in hue,
Could make me any summer's story tell,
Or from their proud lap pluck them where they grew:
Nor did I wonder at the lily's white,
Nor praise the deep vermilion in the rose;
They were but sweet, but figures of delight,
Drawn after you, you pattern of all those.
     Yet seem'd it winter still, and, you away,
     As with your shadow I with these did play.

William Shakespeare

ANTHONY

Your absent name at roll call was more present
than you ever were, forever
on parole in the back of the class.
The first morning you were gone
We practised penmanship to keep our minds
off you. My first
uncoiled chains of connecting circles,
oscilloscopic hills;
my carved-up desk, rippled as a wash-board.

A train cut you in half in the Jersey marshes.
You played there after school.
I thought of you and felt afraid.
One awkward 'a' multiplied into a fence
running across the page.
I copied out two rows of 'b's'.
The caboose of the last 'a' ran smack against
the margin. Nobody even liked you!
My 'e's' and 'f's' travelled over the snowy landscape
on parallel tracks—the blue guidelines
that kept our letters even.

The magician sawed his wife in half.
He passed his hand through the gulf of air
Where her waist should be.
Divided into two boxes she turned and smiled
and all her ten toes flexed.
I skipped a line.
I dotted the disconnected body of each 'i'.

At the bottom of the page
I wrote your name. Erased it.
Wrote it, and erased again.

Jane Shore

A FEW QUESTIONS ABOUT ROMEO

And what if Romeo,
lying in that chapel in Verona,
miserable and spotty, at odds with everything,
what if he'd had a revelation from which
Juliet was absent?
What if, just before darkness settled
the arguments between most things,
through a gap in the walls he'd seen
a garden exploding,
and the pink shadow of blossom
shivering on stones?
What if,
unromantic as it seems,
her mouth, eyes, cheeks and breasts suddenly became
ornaments on a frame
common as any girl's?

Could he still have drunk that potion had he known
without her the world still glowed
and love was not confined
in one shape alone?

From the prison the weary imagine
all living things inhabit
how could either
not have wished to escape?
Poor Romeo, poor Juliet, poor human race!

Brian Patten

MARGINALIA

When it was Munich, I was eight.
Miss Adams made her point like this:
'Without a ruler, no one can
Draw me a line that's truly straight.'
And thus, to make her meaning plain:
'Not even any famous man:
Herr Hitler. Mr Chamberlain.'

And through the years, one might infer,
Miss Adams used such other names
As fitted best the days she came
To teach this truth, beloved of her:
'Not even Mr Stalin, and
Sir Winston Churchill, he's the same,
Could draw me one straight line freehand.'

And I should think that through that door,
In one of those brown passages,
I might still find her echoing room
Somewhere along the lower floor;
And hear again that doctrine taught,
To forty different minds for whom
It would seem just as strange a thought.

'No one who thinks that he can draw
Straight lines without a ruler, will
Ever surprise me if he fails –
What do you think your ruler's *for*?
There isn't anyone at all
Could do it. Not the Prince of Wales!
Not even General de Gaulle!'

Alan Brownjohn

FATIMA

Class, this is Fatima
all the way from —
who can spell Bosnia for me?

I know if she could speak
English, she would tell us
what a lucky girl she feels
to be here in Bromley — THIS IS BROMLEY —
while all her friends
had to stay behind in —
who can spell Sarajevo for me?

This morning we are going to carry on
with our Nativity Play For Today.
Fatima has lovely blonde hair — HAIR —
so she is going to play the Virgin Mary;
then she won't have to say anything.
No sulking, Lisa; you can be
the landlady. She's got a nice rude speech
and a shiny handbag.

Alex is Joseph; you other boys
are soldiers. But remember
you're not to get carried away
killing the babies. This is acting.

Fatima, sit here, dear;
this is your baby — BABY.
Joseph, put your hand on her shoulder.
Now, angel chorus, let's have the first verse
of 'Hope for the world, peace evermore.'
Herod, stop fidgeting with your kalashnikov.
Fatima, why are you crying?

Carole Satyamurti

ON SETTING MY CLASS THEIR FIRST QUIZ

Fifty-three faces, sad and apprehensive,
The boys in jeans attired, with flat-topped hair,
The girls more gaily dressed, and more expensive —
More frightening, and more fair —

All sit with pen in hand and book on knee,
Prepared to write, uncertain what to say,
All hating Coleridge, and loathing me,
Wishing the hour away.

My dears, I will not quiz you any more,
You shall be graded only for your faces...
You, sirs, I'll grade for patience and cropped skull.

I never passed so long an hour before! —
But surely somewhere in you there are traces
Of Blake and Wordsworth, though I make them dull?

Kenneth Hopkins

BIRD IN THE CLASSROOM

The students drowsed and drowned
In the teacher's ponderous monotone –
Limp bodies looping in the wordy heat,
Melted and run together, desks and flesh as one,
Swooning and swimming in a sea of drone.

Each one asleep, swayed and vaguely drifted
With lidding eyes and lolling, weighted heads,
Was caught on heavy waves and dimly lifted,
Sunk slowly, ears ringing, in the syrup of his sound,
Or borne from the room on a heaving wilderness of beds.

And then, on a sudden, a bird's cool voice
Punched out song. Crisp and spare
On the startled air,
Beak-beamed
Or idly tossed,
Each note gleamed
Like a bead of frost.

A bird's cool voice from a neighbour tree
With five clear calls – mere grains of sound
Rare and neat
Repeated twice...
But they sprang the heat
Like drops of ice.

Ears cocked, before the comment ran
Fading and chuckling where a wattle stirred,
The students wondered how they could have heard
Such dreary monotones from man,
Such wisdom from a bird.

Colin Thiele

CEDAR TREE

Light filtered through the cedar
In the Headmaster's garden,
A garden never to be trodden,
On to the heads of clumsy adolescents
And desks with Racine or Virgil open.

There would always, it seemed, be time for books.
To all intents and purposes
We were secure.
No one would seriously question
The presence of poetry or the presence of God.
Teachers would be succeeded by other teachers
And then I would teach, perhaps, and certainly write

Contentedly in a safe house
With a gentle wife ministering to me,
And beyond the garden and the deep wood,
At least in most cases,
Dignity and faith would regulate
Business and government. The box of pencils

Was also of cedar and its quiet scent
Was reassuring, too. I trusted.
Praise to the tree, I thought, praise to the tree

That reaches up into the firmament
But anchors firmly in the kindly soil
And spreads its boughs to shelter the whole earth.

John Adlard.

THE SHADOW ON THE MAP

How do I know? Why, one afternoon
Miss Pallant (geography) all on her own
With her back to a pearl-coloured polythene moon
That peered through the chalk-dusted windowpane
Had drawn on the blackboard a large map of Spain...

The chalk it squeaked and the clock it ticked
Ever so peaceful and matter-of-fact
As her slender arm's shadow slipped and crept
Over Castile — when somebody stepped
Quickly behind Miss Pallant and tacked
Her shadow to Spain — what a devilish act!

Pinned like a moth by her shadow, Miss Pallant
Tore herself loose to defy her assailant
Only to find the room empty and silent!

Who could have been so invisibly violent?

No one can answer. But how can she feel
With never a shadow to follow her trail
Never a shadow to follow at heel
Whether the sunlight be brilliant or pale.

And still hangs her shadow, as proof of my tale
Dusty and wan, on the map of Castile!

Joan Aiken

CATHERINE'S STORY

I flung my satchel out of the window
Of our dorm, up to the sky,
Up on to a horn of the moon, I swear
I saw it hanging in the spangled air,
And I thought what a story I should have to tell.
    But next morning
It wasn't hanging on the horn of the moon,
    It was hanging there
    In the misty air,
    Out of my reach,
    On a very plane tree.
    Our dorm window
    Opens on the foam
    Of perilous trees
    Where our mistresses roam,
    It's the Head's private garden.
And then old Mr Beasley, the gardener, came by.

Measly Mr Beasley settled for a chat.
    I wouldn't have minded that
    But the chat he settled for
    Was with our Head,
        Miss Stead.
She looked up at my satchel, and saw me.
    'Catherine, did you throw that?' she asked.
    'Yes, Miss Stead,' I had to reply,
        And she said, 'Why?'
'I flung it on to a horn of the Moon,' I said,
    'But it must have fallen down
    On to a branch of that tree,' I said.
    'I see,' said the Head.

'Catherine, you're a moony child,' she said.
      'I like your fancy and, indeed,
      You're not the first to see
      In the Moon a vehicle for poetry;
The loyal moon whose face
Is never turned away from man.
      But nevertheless, you can
      Hardly expect to choose
      To use, indeed to abuse,
A sickle moon as a peg for a satchel.
      So do not again, I beg,
      Treat with such levity our as yet
      Unconquered satellite.'

      'And lest you should forget,'
          Went on the Head,
      'Your error of last night,'
          She sternly said,
      'You will this evening write
An account of this incident for the School Magazine
And bring it me tomorrow.
      Now, are you dressed?'
      'No, Miss Stead,' I confessed.
'Then hurry, or you'll be late for prayers,' she said.

At prayers she read us from Corinthians One.
      'There is one glory of the Sun
      And another glory of the Moon,'
          She read,
      Our darling Head, Miss Stead.

Geoffrey Dearmer

WHY WE NEED LIBRARIES

It is the mid-sixties, and it
does not matter which year exactly;

it may have been the year Mrs White
threw water on the cat. It may not.

At the bottom of the hill, opposite
the football factory which will close

in 1981 (although nobody knows this
because nobody can look into the future

in fact the future is a pair
of stout walking boots in a sealed box)

they are loading books from the old
library to take to the new library

which is near the new clinic and not
far from the new old folks' home

at the top of the hill. Yes, isn't
it symbolic that these new things are

at the top of the hill. Yes, isn't
that Ian McMillan and his pal Chris

Allatt waiting outside the empty new
library, the green tickets in their

fists, their eyes hungry for Biggles?
It is the mid-sixties, and the future

is waiting to walk away from us, briskly,
as though we smell funny, leaving the new

library to darken and crack into the old
library, closed on Saturday afternoons

Everyman I will go with thee and be thy
guide except on Saturday afternoons and

sometimes all day Mondays and sometimes
certain days for the need of money to pay

the people who open the doors to let the books
out. You never know what will happen, though,

because the future is a book in a private
library. Unless we can request that book

and borrow it and read it and read it.

Ian McMillan

IN THE PUBLIC LIBRARY

The infant, while his mother peers at novels,
Sings of a black sheep and its cry and fleece.
She doesn't seem to worry that he grovels
In mucky footprints and the parquet's grease.

I have to step across the raucous singer
(Anorak making him still more obese.)
I could, but don't, tread on his grubby finger;
Though let him see my face – a cruel crook's.

I only hope his life will gain from books.

Roy Fuller

THE O-FILLER

One noon in the library, I watched a man —
imagine! — filling in O's, a little, rumpled
nobody of a man, who licked his stub of pencil
and leaned over every O with a loving care,
shading it neatly, exactly to its edges
until the open pages
were pocked and dotted with solid O's, like towns
and capitals on a map. And yet, so peppered,
the book appeared inhabited and complete.

That whole afternoon, as the light outside softened
and the library groaned woodenly,
he worked and worked, his o-so-patient shading
descending like an eyelid over each open O
for page after page. Not once did he miss one,
or hover even a moment over an *a*
or an *e* or a *p* or a *g*. Only the O's —
oodles of O's, O's multitudinous, O's manifold,
O's italic and roman.
And what light on his crumpled face when he discovered —
as I supposed — odd words like *zoo* and *ooze*,
polo, oolong and *odontology*!

Think now. In that limitless library,
all round the steep-shelved walls, bulging in their bindings,
books stood, waiting. Heaven knows how many
he had so far filled, but still there remained
uncountable volumes of O-laden prose, and odes
with inflated capital O's (in the manner of Shelley),
O-bearing Bibles and biographies,
even whole sections devoted to O alone,
all his for the filling. Glory, glory, glory!

How utterly open and endless the world must have seemed to him,
how round and ample! Think of it. A pencil
was all he needed. Life was one wide O.

And why, at the end of things, should O's not be closed
as eyes are? I envied him, for in my place
across the table from him, had I accomplished
anything as firm as he had, or as fruitful?
What could I show? A handful of scrawled lines,
an afternoon yawned and wondered away,
and a growing realisation that in time
even my scribbled words would come
under his grubby thumb, and the blinds be drawn
on all my O's, with only this thought for comfort —
that when he comes to this poem, a proper joy
may amaze his wizened face and, o, a pure pleasure
make his meticulous pencil quiver.

Alastair Reid

EX LIBRIS

'Jane Searle, her book' the scrap of paper says;
Above the words a smiling cupid plays;
The book Jane owned in seventeen–eighty-four? —
Search after Happiness, by Hannah More;
This moral work perhaps she understood,
And — better still — perhaps it did her good.
How did Jane look, speak, live, those years ago?
— This was her book, and that is all we know.

Anon

TREAD SOFTLY

Tread softly here, as ye would tread
In presence of the honoured dead,
With reverent step and low-bowed head.

Speak low, as low as ye would speak
Before some saint of grandeur meek
Whose favour ye would humbly seek.

Within these walls the very air
Seems weighted with a fragrance rare,
Like incense burned at evening prayer.

Here may we sit and converse hold
With those whose names in ages old
Were in the book of fame enrolled.

Here under poet's power intense
We leave the world of sound and sense,
Where mortals strive with problems dense,

And mount to realms where fancy, free,
Above our poor humanity,
Roams in a joyous ecstasy.

Or if through history's maze we tread,
The hero, patriot, long since dead,
Whose great heart for his country bled,

Seems once again to work and fight
In superstition's darkest night
For God, his fellows, and the right.

Enough! mere words can never tell
The influence of the grateful spell
Which seems among these books to dwell.

Anon

7 · *Sea-Sand and Sorrow*

Almost as soon as morning shone upon the oyster-shell frame of my mirror I was out of bed, and out with little Em'ly, picking up stones upon the beach.

"You're quite a sailor, I suppose?" I said to Em'ly. I don't know that I supposed anything of the kind, but I felt it an act of gallantry to say something; and a shining sail close to us made such a pretty little image of itself, at the moment, in her bright eye, that it came into my head to say this.

"No," replied Em'ly, shaking her head, "I'm afraid of the sea."

"Afraid!" I said, with a becoming air of boldness, and looking very big at the mighty ocean. "*I* an't!"

"Ah! but it's cruel," said Em'ly. "I have seen it very cruel to some of our men. I have seen it tear a boat as big as our house all to pieces."

"I hope it wasn't the boat that ——"

"That father was drownded in?" said Em'ly. "No. Not that one, I never see that boat."

"Nor him?" I asked her.

Little Em'ly shook her head. "Not to remember!"

Charles Dickens: DAVID COPPERFIELD.

...and above all there was Whitsand Bay, about a mile and a half off. It was then a really solitary bit of waste, a cliff descending from a field. There was a rough path leading to an exquisite beach of white sand, over which curled and dashed waves from the Atlantic, bringing in razor shells, tellinas of a delicate pink, cockles, and mactras. It was the most delicious place that I ever knew, and to this hour a windy night will make me dream of the roll and dash of its waves and the delight of those sands.

Charlotte Yonge: AUTOBIOGRAPHY

THE TIDE IN THE RIVER

The tide in the river,
The tide in the river,
The tide in the river runs deep.
I saw a shiver
Pass over the river
As the tide turned in its sleep.

Eleanor Farjeon

SUMMER BEACH

For how long known this boundless wash of light,
   This smell of purity, this gleaming waste,
This wind? This brown, strewn wrack how old a sight,
   These pebbles round to touch and salt to taste.

See, the slow marbled heave, the liquid arch,
   Before the waves' procession to the land
Flowers in foam; the ripples' onward march,
   Their last caresses on the pure hard sand.

For how long known these bleaching corks, new-made
   Smooth and enchanted from the lapping sea?
Since first I laboured with a wooden spade
   Against this background of Eternity.

Frances Cornford

WHAT ARE HEAVY?

What are heavy? Sea-sand and sorrow;
What are brief? Today and tomorrow;
What are frail? Spring blossoms and youth;
What are deep? The ocean and truth.

Christina Rossetti

SEA-FEVER

I must go down to the seas again, to the lonely sea and the sky,
And all I ask is a tall ship and a star to steer her by,
And the wheel's kick and the wind's song and the white sail's shaking,
And a grey mist on the sea's face and a grey dawn breaking.

I must go down to the seas again, for the call of the running tide
Is a wild call and a clear call that may not be denied;
And all I ask is a windy day with the white clouds flying,
And the flung spray and the blown spume, and the sea-gulls crying.

I must go down to the seas again, to the vagrant gypsy life,
To the gull's way and the whale's way where the wind's like a whetted
     knife;
And all I ask is a merry yarn from a laughing fellow-rover,
And quiet sleep and a sweet dream when the long trick's over.

John Masefield

CORNISH WAKING

A sea-bird's shadow went across the wall;
  My bedroom faced the sea,
A wordless thought I never shall recall
  Escaped scot-free.

Frances Cornford

THE BLACK PEBBLE

There went three children down to the shore,
  Down to the shore and back;
There was skipping Susan and bright-eyed Sam
  And little scowling Jack.

Susan found a white cockle-shell,
  The prettiest ever seen,
And Sam picked up a piece of glass
  Rounded and smooth and green.

But Jack found only a plain black pebble
  That lay by the rolling sea,
And that was all that ever he found;
  So back they went all three.

The cockle-shell they put on the table,
  The green glass on the shelf,
But the little black pebble that Jack had found,
  He kept it for himself.

James Reeves

maggie and milly and molly and may
went down to the beach(to play one day)

and maggie discovered a shell that sang
so sweetly she couldn't remember her troubles,and

milly befriended a stranded star
whose rays five languid fingers were;

and molly was chased by a horrible thing
which raced sideways while blowing bubbles:and

may came home with a smooth round stone
as small as a world and as large as alone.

For whatever we lose(like a you or a me)
it's always ourselves we find in the sea

e. e. cummings

A VERY ODD FISH

Granny and I with dear Dadu,
Went rambling on the shore;
With pebbles smooth and cockleshells
We filled his pinafore.

Beneath the stones and in the pool
We found, to our delight,
Shrimps, periwinkles, and a most
Voracious appetite.

D'Arcy Wentworth Thompson

EAST ANGLIAN BATHE

Oh when the early morning at the seaside
  Took us with hurrying steps from Horsey Mere
To see the whistling bent-grass on the leeside
  And then the tumbled breaker-line appear,
On high, the clouds with mighty adumbration
  Sailed over us to seaward fast and clear
And jellyfish in quivering isolation
  Lay silted in the dry sand of the breeze
And we, along the table-land of beach blown
  Went gooseflesh from our shoulders to our knees
And ran to catch the football, each to each thrown,
  In the soft and swirling music of the seas.

There splashed about our ankles as we waded
  Those intersecting wavelets morning-cold,
And sudden dark a patch of sea was shaded,
  And sudden light another patch would hold
The warmth of whirling atoms in a sun-shot
  And underwater sandstorm green and gold.
So in we dived and louder than a gunshot
  Sea-water broke in fountains down the ear.
How cold the swim, how chattering cold the drying,
  How welcoming the inland reeds appear,
The wood-smoke and the breakfast and the frying,
  And your warm freshwater ripples, Horsey Mere.

John Betjeman

SHADOWS ON BANTWICK SAND

Still morning!
The first faint breakfast-smells
From the long line of Bantwick shore-hotels
Come beachward to find me;
And I stand
Alone on Bantwick sand,
And as the sun broadens behind me,
My long black shadow runs flatly out –
Out to the sea and the far rocks,
Where the fishermen lift their lobster-pots,
Their boats quietly chugging
In the still morning.

Cool evening!
Out in the bay, by the far rocks,
Where the fishermen bait their lobster-pots,
The broad sun sends its level rays
Shoreward to blind me;
And I stand
Alone on Bantwick sand,
And my shadow unrolls behind me:
Back to the land it stretches
A dark finger, and reaches
To the old stone house where we've always stayed,
Where the windows are open, the savoury dishes ready,
The silver, the white cloth laid –
In the cool evening.

John Walsh

BOURNEMOUTH, SEPTEMBER 3rd, 1939

My summer ends, and term begins next week.
Why am I here in Bournemouth, with my aunt
And 'Uncle Bill', who something tells me can't
Be really my uncle? People speak
In hushed, excited tones. Down on the beach
An aeroplane comes in low over the sea
And there's a scattering as people reach
For towels and picnic gear and books, and flee
Towards the esplanade. Back at the hotel
We hear what the Prime Minister has said.
'So it's begun.' 'Yes, it was bound to.' 'Well,
Give it till Christmas.' Later, tucked in bed,
I hear the safe sea roll and wipe away
The castles I had built in sand that day.

Anthony Thwaite

THE CONSCRIPT

In summer months when he was four
  And used a wooden spade,
Bill Turner floated from this shore
  The boats his father made.

Now he, a soldier, sails from home
  On wild December ways,
Remembering the gentle foam
  And those protected days.

Frances Cornford

SEASIDE

Swiftly out from the friendly lilt of the band,
  The crowd's good laughter, the loved eyes of men,
  I am drawn nightward; I must turn again
Where, down beyond the low untrodden strand,
There curves and glimmers outward to the unknown
  The old unquiet ocean. All the shade
Is rife with magic and movement. I stray alone
  Here on the edge of silence, half afraid,

Waiting a sign. In the deep heart of me
The sullen waters swell towards the moon,
And all my tides set seaward.
                            From inland
Leaps a gay fragment of some mocking tune,
That tinkles and laughs and fades along the sand,
And dies between the seawall and the sea.

Rupert Brooke

CONSULTING SUMMER'S CLOCK

Consulting summer's clock,
But half the hours remain.
I ascertain it with a shock –
I shall not look again.
The second half of joy
Is shorter than the first.
The truth I do not dare to know
I muffle with a jest.

Emily Dickinson

SOMETHING THIS FOGGY DAY

Something this foggy day, a something which
  Is neither of this fog nor of today,
  Has set me dreaming of the winds that play
Past certain cliffs, along one certain beach,
    And turn the topmost edge of waves to spray:
  Ah pleasant pebbly strand so far away,
So out of reach while quite within my reach,
  As out of reach as India or Cathay!
I am sick of where I am and where I am not,
  I am sick of foresight and of memory,
  I am sick of all I have and all I see,
    I am sick of self, and there is nothing new;
Oh weary impatient patience of my lot!—
    Thus with myself: how fares it, Friends, with you?

Christina Rossetti

ACQUAINTED WITH THE NIGHT

I have been one acquainted with the night.
I have walked out in rain – and back in rain.
I have outwalked the furthest city light.

I have looked down the saddest city lane.
I have passed by the watchman on his beat
And dropped my eyes, unwilling to explain.

I have stood still and stopped the sound of feet
When far away an interrupted cry
Came over houses from another street,

But not to call me back or say goodbye;
And further still at an unearthly height,
One luminary clock against the sky
Proclaimed the time was neither wrong nor right.
I have been one acquainted with the night.

Robert Frost

OWL

As I was sitting, late last night,
At my desk by the window, trying to write,

Trying to find the phrase, the word,
To make the poem come right, I heard

The screech of an owl, and saw him streak
Down to strike with claw and beak,

Then turn, with churning wings, to rise
Into the echoes of his cries.

When he was out of sight, I sank
Back in my chair, pushing the blank

Sheets of paper aside and then
Turned out the lamp, put down my pen,

And sat in the dark to think of the owl,
Who is guileless, neither kind nor cruel,

Who lives without the need for thought
And hunts with skills that can't be taught,

Who kills without hatred, without guilt
Strips the flesh from the furry pelt,

Caring nothing at all for words
And nothing at all for the writers of words.

David Harsent

THE KNOWLEDGEABLE CHILD

I always see, — I don't know why, —
If any person's going to die.

That's why nobody talks to me.
There was a man who came to tea,

And when I saw that he would die
I went to him and said 'Good-bye,

'I shall not see you any more.'
He died that evening. Then, next door,

They had a little girl: she died
Nearly as quick, and Mummy cried

And cried; and ever since that day
She's made me promise not to say.

But folks are still afraid of me,
And, where they've children, nobody

Will let me next or nigh to them
For fear I'll say good-bye to them.

L. A. G. Strong

THE QUILT

That day we said goodbye to her,
Winter at work outside, the fire-flecked room
No louder than the black cat's purr
Breathing the way to her doom,
I saw it lying, solid and smooth there,
Her patchwork quilt,
A huge and dangling square,
Triangles of white, oblongs of red,
With bits from curtain and kilt.
I thought it looked just like
A landscape of little fields, seen
In springtime from an aeroplane,
Or, with dots of orange-green,
The mottled back of some big river pike.
And there were strips of calico in that counterpane,
Flannel from a grey Welsh shirt,
A blue velvet diamond, some sprigged lawn,
Faded pieces of a gingham skirt.
And as we slowly watched the dawn
Chequering the vast and empty sky,
'That was my wedding dress' she softly said,
Placing her fingers on one silky hexagon;
She smiled, and finished with a sigh,
The fingers stiffened, the old head bowed.
Before we left, my grandmother had gone,
And married on that morning to the dead,
Lay calm and beautiful in her quilted shroud.

Leonard Clark

BY ST THOMAS WATER

By St Thomas Water
Where the river is thin
We looked for a jam-jar
To catch the quick fish in.
Through St Thomas Churchyard
Jessie and I ran
The day we took the jam-pot
Off the dead man.

On the scuffed tombstone
The grey flowers fell,
Cracked was the water,
Silent the shell.
The snake for an emblem
Swirled on the slab,
Across the beach of sky the sun
Crawled like a crab.

'If we walk,' said Jessie,
'Seven times round,
We shall hear a dead man
Speaking underground.'
Round the stone we danced, we sang,
Watched the sun drop,
Laid our heads and listened
At the tomb-top.

Soft as the thunder
At the storm's start
I heard a voice as clear as blood,
Strong as the heart.
But what words were spoken
I can never say,
I shut my fingers round my head,
Drove them away.

'What are those letters, Jessie,
Cut so sharp and trim
All round this holy stone
With earth up to the brim?'
Jessie traced the letters
Black as coffin-lead.
'He is not dead but sleeping,'
Slowly she said.

I looked at Jessie,
Jessie looked at me,
And our eyes in wonder
Grew wide as the sea.
Past the green and bending stones
We fled hand in hand,
Silent through the tongues of grass
To the river strand.

By the creaking cypress
We moved as soft as smoke
For fear all the people
Underneath awoke.
Over all the sleepers
We darted light as snow
In case they opened up their eyes,
Called us from below.

Many a day has faltered
Into many a year
Since the dead awoke and spoke
And we would not hear.
Waiting in the cold grass
Under a crinkled bough,
Quiet stone, cautious stone,
What do you tell me now?

Charles Causley

SONG

When I am dead, my dearest,
  Sing no sad songs for me;
Plant thou no roses at my head,
  Nor shady cypress tree:
Be the green grass above me
  With showers and dewdrops wet;
And if thou wilt, remember,
  And if thou wilt, forget.

I shall not see the shadows,
  I shall not feel the rain;
I shall not hear the nightingale
  Sing on, as if in pain:
And dreaming through the twilight
  That doth not rise nor set,
Haply I may remember,
  And haply may forget.

Christina Rossetti

UPON A CHILD. AN EPITAPH.

But borne, and like a short Delight,
I glided by my Parents sight.
That done, the harder Fates deny'd
My longer stay, and so I dy'd.

If pittying my sad Parents Teares,
You'l spil a tear, or two with theirs:
And with some flowrs my grave bestrew,
Love and they'l thank you for't. Adieu.

Robert Herrick

THE CHILD DYING

Unfriendly friendly universe,
I pack your stars into my purse,
And bid you, bid you so farewell.
That I can leave you, quite go out,
Go out, go out beyond all doubt,
My father says, is the miracle.

You are so great, and I so small:
I am nothing, you are all:
Being nothing, I can take this way.
Oh I need neither rise nor fall,
For when I do not move at all
I shall be out of all your day.

It's said some memory will remain
In the other place, grass in the rain,
Light on the land, sun on the sea,
A flitting grace, a phantom face,
But the world is out. There is no place
Where it and its ghost can ever be.

Father, father, I dread this air
Blown from the far side of despair,
The cold cold corner. What house, what hold,
What hand is there? I look and see
Nothing-filled eternity,
And the great round world grows weak and old.

Hold my hand, oh hold it fast —
I am changing! — until at last
My hand in yours no more will change,
Though yours change on. You here, I there,
So hand in hand, twin-leafed despair —
I did not know death was so strange.

Edwin Muir

ENDS MEET

My grandmother came down the steps into the garden.
She shone in the gauzy air.
She said: 'There's an old woman at the gate –
See what she wants, my dear.'

My grandmother's eyes were blue like the damsels
Darting and swerving above the stream,
Or like the kingfisher arrow shot into darkness
Through the archway's dripping gleam.

My grandmother's hair was silver as sunlight.
The sun had been poured right over her, I saw,
And ran down her dress and spread a pool for her shadow
To float in. And she would live for evermore.

There was nobody at the gate when I got there.
Not even a shadow hauling along the road,
Nor my yellow snail delicate under the ivy,
Nor my sheltering cold-stone toad.

But the sunflowers aloft were calm. They'd seen no one.
They were sucking light, for ever and a day.
So I busied myself with going away unheeded
And with having nothing to say.

No comment, nothing to tell, or to think,
Whilst the day followed the homing sun.
There was no old woman at my grandmother's gate.

And there isn't at mine.

Frances Bellerby

SPEAKING PROPERLY
(for Charles Tomlinson)

There can be no going back now
to my Russian gran
snapped in the back yard one summer
shy and untidy and still in her apron
as if a moment was all could be taken
from cooking and cleaning and washing for ten.
My great-gran's down in the basement
hid in her orthodox wig and her Yiddish.

As a child I thought theirs the exodus
after Moses, saw them coming like Cossacks
on husky-pulled sledges in icicled furs.
They were my romantic ancestors
who mortified my mum with their foreign ways,
their Vees and their Vyes and their Vobble-yous,
the X on the nationalisation papers
that listed the men and the children
but left out the wives. We turned

our backs on them, put up lace curtains
like the Berlin wall, went off to the shires
to learn to speak nicely and only later
felt their loss. I'd think of great-gran
home-sick for Riga, and heart-sick myself
for a *mama-loshen**, try to raise her ghost
and ask a few questions. She'd haunt
but not answer. Now, writing her off,
I understand why. She who'd had words
with Moses – Ai-yi-yi! – what had she to say
to me, born continents away, born yesterday.

Diana Hendry

* *mama-loshen* . . . mother tongue

AUNT JULIA

Aunt Julia spoke Gaelic
very loud and very fast.
I could not answer her –
I could not understand her.

She wore men's boots
when she wore any.
– I can see her strong foot,
stained with peat,
paddling with the treadle of the spinningwheel
while her right hand drew yarn
marvellously out of the air.

Hers was the only house
where I've lain at night
in the absolute darkness
of a box bed, listening to
crickets being friendly.

She was buckets
and water flouncing into them.
She was winds pouring wetly
round house-ends.
She was brown eggs, black skirts
and a keeper of threepennybits
in a teapot.

Aunt Julia spoke Gaelic
very loud and very fast.
By the time I had learned
a little, she lay
silenced in the absolute black
of a sandy grave

at Luskentyre.
But I hear her still, welcoming me
with a seagull's voice
across a hundred yards
of peatscrapes and lazybeds
and getting angry, getting angry
with so many questions
unanswered.

Norman MacCaig

FRAGMENT

The babe is at peace within the womb;
The corpse is at rest within the tomb:
   We begin in what we end.

Percy Bysshe Shelley

SONG (4)
(for Guy Davenport)

Within the circles of our lives
we dance the circles of the years,
the circles of the seasons
within the circles of the years,
the cycles of the moon

within the circles of the seasons,
the circles of our reasons
within the cycles of the moon.

Again, again we come and go,
changed, changing. Hands
join, unjoin in love and fear,
grief and joy. The circles turn,
each giving into each, into all.
Only music keeps us here,

each by all the others held.
In the hold of hands and eyes
we turn in pairs, that joining
joining each to all again.

And then we turn aside, alone,
out of the sunlight gone

into the darker circles of return.

Wendell Berry

8 · *Play the tune again*

It is argued now that stage life is bad for a young child, and children are not allowed by law to go on the stage until they are ten years old – quite a mature age in my young days! I cannot discuss the whole question here, and must content myself with saying that during my three years at the Princess's I was a very strong, happy, and healthy child. I was never out of the bill except during the run of "A Midsummer Night's Dream", when, through an unfortunate accident, I broke my toe. I was playing Puck, my second part on any stage, and had come up through a trap at the end of the last act to give the final speech. My sister Kate was playing Titania that night as understudy to Carlotta Leclercq. Up I came – but not quite up, for the man shut the trap-door too soon and caught my toe. I screamed. Kate rushed to me and banged her foot on the stage, but the man only closed the trap tighter, mistaking the signal.

"Oh, Katie! Katie!" I cried. "Oh, Nelly! Nelly!" said poor Kate helplessly. Then Mrs. Kean came rushing on and made them open the trap and release my poor foot.

"Finish the play, dear," she whispered excitedly, "and I'll double your salary!" There was Kate holding me up on one side and Mrs. Kean on the other. Well, I did finish the play in a fashion. The text ran something like this –

> If we shadows have offended (Oh, Katie, Katie!)
> Think but this, and all is mended, (Oh, my toe!)
> That you have but slumbered here,
> While these visions did appear. (I can't, I can't!)
> And this weak and idle theme,
> No more yielding but a dream, (Oh, dear! oh, dear!)
> Gentles, do not reprehend; (A big sob)
> If you pardon, we will mend. (Oh, Mrs. Kean!)

Ellen Terry: THE STORY OF MY LIFE

Just before the outbreak of the first world war, I was taken by my parents – both ardent playgoers (dress circle for them; queues for the pit or gallery for us children) – to see the Granville Barker production of A Midsummer Night's Dream at the Savoy Theatre. Though I was only seven or eight, I still remember it very vividly. The gold fairies, a boisterous scarlet Puck, and the wood scenes – gauze curtains with a circular flowery wreath hanging over Titania's bower...

John Gielgud

THE SHADE CATCHERS

I think they were about as high
As haycocks are. They went running by
Catching bits of shade in the sunny street:
'I've got one,' cried sister to brother,
   'I've got two.' 'Now I've got another.'
But scudding away on their little bare feet,
They left the shade in the sunny street.

Charlotte Mew

A PIPER

A piper in the streets to-day
Set up, and tuned, and started to play,
And away, away, away on the tide
Of his music we started; on every side
Doors and windows were opened wide,
And men left down their work and came,
And women with petticoats coloured like flame.
And little bare feet that were blue with cold,
Went dancing back to the age of gold,
And all the world went gay, went gay,
For half an hour in the street to-day.

Seamus O'Sullivan

THE LITTLE DANCERS

Lonely, save for a few faint stars, the sky
Dreams; and lonely, below, the little street
Into its gloom retires, secluded and shy.
Scarcely the dumb roar enters this soft retreat;
And all is dark, save where come flooding rays
From a tavern window: there, to the brisk measure
Of an organ that down in an alley merrily plays,
Two children, all alone and no one by,
Holding their tattered frocks, through an airy maze
Of motion, lightly threaded with nimble feet,
Dance sedately: face to face they gaze,
Their eyes shining, grave with a perfect pleasure.

Laurence Binyon

Hey, nonny no!
Men are fools that wish to die!
Is't not fine to dance and sing
When the bells of death do ring?
Is't not fine to swim in wine,
And turn upon the toe,
And sing *Hey nonny no!*

When the winds blow and the seas flow?
  Hey, nonny no!

DANCING CLASS

Do not expect your child to be a genius,
a season's buds uncurl before one rare
new rose amazes. Watch when curious

green calyx opens, folded rhythm swells
crescendo, climax, movement scatters air.
Frilled petals, upright stem, colour foretells

summer's young talent, poised in confidence,
sheltered with rain and wind, nourished with care.
Sunshine drops glitter on the practice dance.

Do not expect a rose to last for ever,
maturing quickly, perfumed, unaware
that spotted death or hidden grub can mar.

When genius flowers, let children gather round
marvelling at strange texture; one may dare
to snatch a leaf, crumple in jealous hand.

Alison Bielski

Dance to your daddie,
My bonnie laddie,
Dance to your daddie, and to your mammie sing!
You shall get a coatie,
And a pair of breekies,
You shall get a coatie when the boat comes in!

DANCING CLASS

Now we're all going to try again, aren't we girls?
Only this time we know what to expect and no-one's
going to forget that these red shoes spell magic.
Once on, they'll take off. You want to turn right?
They pirouette left. You want *Swan Lake*?
They've taken to tap. Girls, these shoes aren't made
for walking. If you don't have Nerve and Verve,
stay in your slippers. These shoes know more dances
than you've ever dreamt of and what you've got to do
is listen to your feet, then learn to control them.
And about stopping. It isn't a problem.
Just sit on your bum. Now, let's go over the rules:

Number one. Anyone who wants to dance has to leave
home. Number two. No guilt trips into the forest.
Head for Covent Garden or Birmingham City. Number
three. No knocking at the executioner's door asking
for your feet to be chopped off. That's cheating.
Number four. The red shoes are like the best tunes
and we know who they belong to, don't we? Number
five. No hobbling about on crutches feeling sorry
for yourself because you didn't make it to the Bolshoi.

OK? On your toes.

Diana Hendry

SOLOISTS

The awaited moment, the ballerina parts
The chorus and her solo dancing starts.
She is modest and small like the rest. Her rarity
Is in lightness and clarity.

With a silver hammer she strikes each note
Once and singly. Then is carried apart
Or absorbed into the choral dance again.
Her friends take her in.

Again at an awaited moment the solo
Piano's voice will enter the concerto.
In the heart of a forest's multiple murmuring
It rises like a spring,

And the orchestra parts its complexity
To let its tutelary spirit free.
And rests from sound. The cadenza takes its way
Straying, but cannot stray

Out of perfection. And always – far though it runs,
By single notes like the dancer – as it returns
The orchestra will stretch out hands again,
Take its hand, and whirl it in.

E. J. Scovell

Your hands have rituals as old as springtime.
Your hands are birds, climbing the stairs of air.
Your hands are flying silver fish escaping
From what faint shadow, of what threatening, where?

A. S. J. Tessimond

THE CORNER KNOT

I was a child and overwhelmed: Mozart
Had snatched me up fainting and wild at heart
To a green land of wonder, where estranged
I dipped my feet in shallow brooks, I ranged
Rough mountains, and fields yellow with small vetch:
Of which, though long I tried, I could not fetch
One single flower away, nor from the ground
Pocket one pebble of the scores I found
Twinkling enchanted there. So for relief
'I'll corner-knot,' said I, 'this handkerchief,
Faithful familiar that, look, here I shake
In these cool airs for proof that I'm awake.'
I tied the knot, the aspens all around
Heaved, and the river-banks were filled with sound;
Which failing presently, the insistent loud
Clapping of hands returned me to the crowd.
I felt and, fumbling, took away with me
The knotted witness of my ecstasy,
Though flowers and streams were vanished past recall,
The aspens, the bright pebbled reach and all.

But now, grown older, I suspect Mozart
Himself had been snatched up by curious art
To my green land: estranged and wild at heart
He too had crossed the brooks, essayed to pick
That yellow vetch with which the plains are thick;
And being put to it (as I had been)
To smuggle back some witness of the scene,
Had knotted up his cambric handkerchief
With common music, rippling, flat and brief;
And home again, had sighed above the score
'Ay, a remembrancer, but nothing more.'

Robert Graves

W. A. MOZART 1756–1791

When Mozart was a tiny boy,
A scoffer, wishing to annoy,
Dared him to play a wide-spaced chord
Upon his father's harpsichord.
Of course his hands were far too small —
The thing could not be done at all.
But, much to his papa's delight,
He played the top half with his right,
While with his left he struck the bass —
A smile upon his pretty face.
There still remained between the two
A middle note: what would he do?
. . . Yes, it is just as you suppose,
He played it with his little nose.

SIR EDWARD ELGAR, 1857–1934

Try to imagine, if you can,
That ELGAR was a handy man,
And when not writing tunes and airs
Was very fond of mending chairs.
Then he derived much merriment
From chemical experiment.
Another thing you'd often see
Was Elgar cutting down a tree;
And once he made a double-bass
Out of an ancient packing case.
I think this fact sticks out a mile:
Elgar was very versatile.

Helen Henschel

TO A CHILD AT THE PIANO

Play the tune again; but this time
with more regard for the movement at the source of it,
and less attention to time. Time falls
curiously in the course of it.

Play the tune again; not watching
your fingering, but forgetting, letting flow
the sound till it surrounds you. Do not count
or even think. Let go.

Play the tune again; but try to be
nobody, nothing, as though the pace
of the sound were your heart beating, as though
the music were your face.

Play the tune again. It should be easier
to think less every time of the notes, of the measure.
It is all an arrangement of silence. Be silent, and then
play it for your pleasure.

Play the tune again; and this time, when it ends,
do not ask me what I think. Feel what is happening
strangely in the room as the sound glooms over
you, me, everything.

Now,
play the tune again.

Alastair Reid

KATYA PLAYS HAYDN

Katya's fingers on the keys
long and limber take their ease.
Katya's feet beneath the chair
dangle gently in the air.
Harmony loves to abide in
Katya's knees and Joseph Haydn.

Russell Hoban

PIANO

Softly, in the dusk, a woman is singing to me;
Taking me back down the vista of years, till I see
A child sitting under the piano, in the boom of the tingling strings
And pressing the small, poised feet of a mother who smiles as she sings.

In spite of myself, the insidious mastery of song
Betrays me back, till the heart of me weeps to belong
To the old Sunday evenings at home, with winter outside
And hymns in the cosy parlour, the tinkling piano our guide.

So now it is vain for the singer to burst into clamour
With the great black piano appassionato. The glamour
Of childish days is upon me, my manhood is cast
Down in the flood of remembrance. I weep like a child for the past.

D. H. Lawrence

GETTING IT WRONG

I am the eldest. I arrogate roles round here.
Somewhat afraid to be God, I am Gabriel,
my darkhaired penultimate sister can be Mary.
I do not love her. I give her no words to say,
only a doll with a faulty eye, wrapped tight
in a terry nappy, and instructions to act humble.
My brother is Joseph, first King and would have been
Herod only he jibbed at it. My fairhaired sister
(who I love) is chief shepherd and keeper of the inn.
As each she is reverent, always willing,
her voice modulates sweetly and she never cracks up
laughing as Mary, my flesh-thorn sometimes does.
The baby wide-eyed, with a teatowel transforming
his podgy face to boyhood is un- or in- or a-
directable, though he'd die for my archangelic praise.
I love him but it irks when he goes wall-eyed
with bafflement and fear of blame as I spread
my sheeted arms like windmill sails and tell him,
'Look astonished.'

We are nearly and then we are there. The evening.
The door flung open. The perfect moment of surprise
and praise. I have only got as far as the tidings
of great joy with the baby looking almost astonished
and fairhaired sister giving it all she's got of awe
and bloody Mary on the bottom step practising simpers
and Joseph hitching up the dressing-gown by its plaited
cord belt – I've only got that far when Dad smiles
a yawn and Mam says 'I think it's Frankie Howard
on the other channel in a minute.'

A click and less than a second and that oblong face
with its pout lip and suggestive sideglance
fills the dark room with the voice of God,
each syllable stretched elastic. Ooo-er, it says.
The overtones and undertones curl me under my sheet
like a slug. But I'm wondering how we'll stage-
manage the crucifixion come Easter even as I retract
to almost nothing.

Jacqueline Brown

STAGE FRIGHT

The audience is good. A lucky sign.
Yet I am frightened and my heart beats fast.
I've felt like this so many times before
While waiting in the wings with all the cast.
They're talking gaily. Don't they feel the same?
Why can't they feel the tension in the air?
Oh, dear, I want to blow my nose again –
I've smudged my lipstick! Quick! – A glass! My hair!
I simply can't go on. Why do I feel
As though my heart will leave my body soon?
Too late to find an understudy now –
The orchestra is playing the last tune.
What's my first line? You're sure? There is no doubt?
I'm on! Er ... 'Sire, your carriage is without'.

Anne Lewis (aged 14)

THE BOY ACTOR

I can remember. I can remember,
The months of November and December
Were filled for me with peculiar joys
So different from those of other boys
For other boys would be counting the days
Until end of term and holiday times
But I was acting in Christmas plays
While they were taken to pantomimes.
I didn't envy their Eton suits,
Their children's dances and Christmas trees.
My life had wonderful substitutes
For such conventional treats as these.
I didn't envy their country larks,
Their organized games in panelled halls:
While they made snow-men in stately parks
I was counting the curtain calls.

I remember the auditions, the nerve-racking auditions:
Darkened auditorium and empty, dusty stage,
Little girls in ballet dresses practising 'positions',
Gentlemen with pince-nez asking you your age.
Hopefulness and nervousness struggling within you,
Dreading that familiar phrase, 'Thank you dear, no more'.
Straining every muscle, every tendon, every sinew
To do your dance much better than you'd ever done before.
Think of your performance. Never mind the others,
Never mind the pianist, talent must prevail.
Never mind the baleful eyes of other children's mothers
Glaring from the corners and willing you to fail.

I can remember. I can remember.
The months of November and December
Were more significant to me

Than other months could ever be
For they were the months of high romance
When destiny waited on tip-toe,
When every boy actor stood a chance
Of getting into a Christmas show.
Not for me the dubious heaven
Of being some prefect's protégé!
Not for me the Second Eleven.
For me, two performances a day.

Ah those first rehearsals! Only very few lines:
Rushing home to mother, learning them by heart,
'Enter Left through window!' – Dots to mark the cue lines:
'Exit with the others' – Still it *was* a part.
Opening performance; legs a bit unsteady,
Dedicated tension, shivers down my spine,
Powder, grease and eye-black, sticks of make-up ready
Leichner number three and number five and number nine.
World of strange enchantment, magic for a small boy
Dreaming of the future, reaching for the crown,
Rigid in the dressing-room, listening for the call-boy
'Overture Beginners – Everybody Down!'

I can remember. I can remember.
The months of November and December,
Although climatically cold and damp,
Meant more to me than Aladdin's lamp.
I see myself, having got a job,
Walking on wings along the Strand,
Uncertain whether to laugh or sob
And clutching tightly my mother's hand,
I never cared who scored the goal
Or which side won the silver cup,
I never learned to bat or bowl
But I heard the curtain going up.

Noel Coward

THE FORBIDDEN PLAY

I'll tell you the truth, Father, though your heart bleed:
  To the Play I went,
With sixpence for a near seat, money's worth indeed,
  The best ever spent.

You forbade me, you threatened me, but here's the story
  Of my splendid night:
It was colour, drums, music, a tragic glory,
  Fear with delight.

Hamlet, Prince of Denmark, title of the tale:
  He of that name,
A tall, glum fellow, velvet cloaked, with a shirt of mail,
  Two eyes like flame.

All the furies of Hell circled round that man,
  Maddening his heart,
There was old murder done before play began,
  Aye, the ghost took part.

There were grave-diggers delving, they brought up bones,
  And with rage and grief
All the players shouted in full, kingly tones,
  Grand, passing belief.

Ah, there were ladies there radiant as day,
  And changing scenes:
Fabulous words were tossed about like hay
  By kings and queens.

I puzzled on the sense of it in vain,
  Yet for pain I cried,
As one and all they faded, poisoned or slain,
  In great agony died.

Drive me out, Father, never to return,
   Though I am your son,
And penniless! But that glory for which I burn
   Shall be soon begun:

I shall wear great boots, shall strut and shout,
   Keep my locks curled;
The fame of my name shall go ringing about
   Over half the world.

Robert Graves

THE CURTAIN

When the curtain goes down at the end of the play,
The actors and actresses hurry away.

Titania, Bottom, and Quince, being stars,
Can afford to drive home in their own private cars.

Hippolyta, Starveling, and Flute are in luck,
They've been offered a lift in a taxi by Puck;

And Snug and Lysander and Oberon pop
In a bus, and Demetrius clambers on top.

With the chorus of fairies no bus can compete,
So they are obliged to trudge home on their feet:

It seems rather hard on the poor little things,
After flying about all the evening with wings.

Guy Boas

AT THE THEATRE

The sun was bright when we went in,
   But night and lights were there,
The walls had golden trimming on
   And plush on every chair.

The people talked; the music played,
   Then it grew black as pitch,
Yes, black as closets full of clothes,
   Or caves, I don't know which.

The curtain rolled itself away,
   It went I don't know where,
But, oh, that country just beyond,
   I do wish we lived there!

The mountain peaks more jaggéd rise,
   Grass grows more green than here;
The people there have redder cheeks,
   And clothes more gay and queer.

They laugh and smile, but not the same,
   Exactly, as we do.
And if they ever have to cry
   Their tears are different too –

More shiny, somehow, and more sad,
   You hold your breath to see
If everything will come out right
   And they'll live happily;

If Pierrot will kiss Pierrette
   Beneath an orange moon,
And Harlequin and Columbine
   Outwit old Pantaloon.

You know they will, they always do,
  But still your heart must beat,
And you must pray they will be saved,
  And tremble in your seat.

And then it's over and they bow
  All edged about with light,
The curtain rattles down and shuts
  Them every one from sight.

It's strange to find the afternoon
  Still bright outside the door,
And all the people hurrying by
  The way they were before!

Rachel Field

from MACBETH

To-morrow, and to-morrow, and to-morrow,
Creeps in this petty pace from day to day,
To the last syllable of recorded time;
And all our yesterdays have lighted fools
The way to dusty death. Out, out, brief candle!
Life's but a walking shadow; a poor player
That struts and frets his hour upon the stage,
And then is heard no more; it is a tale
Told by an idiot, full of sound and fury,
Signifying nothing.

William Shakespeare

CINDERS

After the pantomime, carrying you back to the car
On the coldest night of the year
My coat, black leather, cracking in the wind.

Through the darkness we are guided by a star
It is the one the Good Fairy gave you
You clutch it tightly, your magic wand.

And I clutch you tightly for fear you blow away
For fear you grow up too soon and – suddenly,
I almost slip, so take it steady down the hill.

Hunched against the wind and hobbling
I could be mistaken for your grandfather
And sensing this, I hold you tighter still.

Knowing that I will never see you dressed for the Ball
Be on hand to warn you against Prince Charmings
And the happy ever afters of pantomime.

On reaching the car I put you into the baby seat
And fumble with straps I have yet to master
Thinking, if only there were more time. More time.

You are crying now. Where is your wand?
Oh no. I can't face going back for it
Let some kid find it in tomorrow's snow.

Waiting in the wings, the witching hour.
Already the car is changing. Smells sweet
Of ripening seed. We must go. Must go.

Roger McGough

from THE RUBAIYAT OF OMAR KHAYAM

For in and out, above, below,
'Tis nothing but a magic shadow-show,
Played in a box whose candle is the sun
Round which we Phantom Figures come and go.

Edward Fitzgerald

from A MIDSUMMER-NIGHT'S DREAM

If we shadows have offended,
Think but this, and all is mended,
That you have but slumber'd here
While these visions did appear.
And this weak and idle theme,
No more yielding but a dream,
Gentles, do not reprehend:
If you pardon, we will mend.
And, as I'm an honest Puck,
If we have unearned luck
Now to 'scape the serpent's tongue,
We will make amends ere long;
Else the Puck a liar call:
So, good night unto you all.
Give me your hands, if we be friends,
And Robin shall restore amends.

William Shakespeare

A MIDSUMMER NIGHT'S DREAM
IN REGENT'S PARK

And what will they remember when
They wake, like Bottom, from their dream?
Will they believe they laughed like this?
And will their restless bodies seem
The same that settled here like dew
Along the benches, in a trance
Of hope and wonder, while old Puck
Led the four lovers through their dance?

The treetops rustle, and the sky
Darkens around a haughty moon.
Cartoon words on homespun lips
Float through the night in their balloon.
Titania curses Oberon
And up the loyal fairies leap.
Within a wood within a wood
The four enchanted lovers sleep.

And will these children ever think
Again about this leaf-lit scene –
Even a single turning branch
Glimmer in their darker green?
Perhaps one moment when the sky
Was dropping dusk light from above
Will touch their eyes with tenderness
Before another night of love.

Derwent May

FRAGMENT OF AN ENGLISH OPERA

(Designed as a model for young librettists)

Dramatis personae:
Father (bass)
Mother (contralto)
Daughter (soprano)

Scene: a room. *Time*: Evening

Father:	Retire, my daughter;
	   Prayers have been said;
	Take your warm water
	   And go to bed.

Daughter:	But I had rather Sit up instead.
Father:	I am your father, So go to bed.
Daughter:	Are you my father?
Father:	I think so, rather: You go to bed.

Mother:	My daughter, vanish;
	   You hear me speak:
	This is not Spanish,
	   Nor is it Greek.

Daughter:	Oh, what a bother! Would I were dead!
Mother:	I am your mother, So go to bed.
Daughter:	Are you my mother?
Mother:	You have no other: You go to bed.
Father:	Take your bed-candle And take it quick. This is the handle.

Daughter:	Is *this* the handle?
Father:	No, that's the wick.
	This is the handle,
	At this end here.
	Take your bed-candle
	And disappear.
Daughter:	Oh dear, oh dear!
Father & Mother:	Take your warm water,
	As we have said;
	You are our daughter,
	So go to bed.
Daughter:	Am I your daughter?
Father & Mother:	If not, you oughter:
	You go to bed.

                    I am their daughter;
                    If not, I oughter:
                       Prayers have been said.
                    This is my mother;
                    I have no other:
                       Would I were dead!
                    That is my father;
                    He thinks so, rather:
                       Oh dear, oh dear!
                    I take my candle;
                    This is the handle:
                       I disappear.

Daughter:

Father & Mother: The coast is clear.

A. E. Housman

9 · *Spell of words*

Aunt Carrie we saw nearly every day as she was a drop-in neighbour and a willing child-minder. Her beauty to me was in the exquisite pattern she made with her lips and her crystal clear voice, whether it was in light-hearted gossip, racy rhymes, profound or magical poetry or her spellbinding story-telling. We were her 'best beloveds' in the *Just So Stories* (which, through requests for repetition, we knew by heart); we, with her, 'went to sea in a sieve', 'gyred and gimbled in the wabe', went 'up the airy mountain, down the rushy glen', and pushed back tears on:

> 'She lived unknown, and few could know
> When Lucy ceased to be;
> But she is in her grave, and oh,
> The difference to me!'

The whole *Golden Treasury* shone pure gold through her scintillating mind. Treasure indeed. Like Walter de la Mare's *Martha:*

> 'Her small dark lovely head,
> Seemed half the meaning
> Of the words she said.'

Christabel Burniston: LIFE IN A LIBERTY BODICE

People sometimes talk of new worlds being opened by poetry but for me *Lepanto* showed me an entrance into a world that I knew to be *mine* and that previously I had only had hints and foreshadowings of – on hot summer nights by the sea, while lying in the sun after a swim, or when listening to triumphant bands playing martial music. I had never realized before that poetry had any connection with such experiences and sensations but from this time onwards I searched in every poem that we read in class for the same thrill I had found in *Lepanto*.

Elizabeth Jennings: LET´S HAVE SOME POETRY

THE COOL WEB

Children are dumb to say how hot the day is,
How hot the scent is of the summer rose,
How dreadful the black wastes of evening sky,
How dreadful the tall soldiers drumming by.

But we have speech, to chill the angry day,
And speech, to dull the rose's cruel scent.
We spell away the overhanging night,
We spell away the soldiers and the fright.

There's a cool web of language winds us in,
Retreat from too much joy or too much fear:
We grow sea-green at last and coldly die
In brininess and volubility.

But if we let our tongues lose self-possession,
Throwing off language and its watery clasp
Before our death, instead of when death comes,
Facing the wide glare of the children's day,
Facing the rose, the dark sky and the drums,
We shall go mad no doubt and die that way.

Robert Graves

from THE PRELUDE

Twice five years
Or less I might have seen, when first my mind
With conscious pleasure opened to the charm
Of words in tuneful order, found them sweet
For their own *sakes*, a passion, and a power...

Willam Wordsworth

WORDS

Out of us all
That make rhymes,
Will you choose
Sometimes—
As the winds use
A crack in a wall
Or a drain,
Their joy or their pain
To whistle through—
Choose me,
You English words?

I know you:
You are light as dreams,
Tough as oak,
Precious as gold,
As poppies and corn,
Or an old cloak:
Sweet as our birds
To the ear,
As the burnet rose
In the heat
Of Midsummer:
Strange as the races
Of dead and unborn:
Strange and sweet
Equally,
And familiar,
To the eye,
As the dearest faces
That a man knows,
And as lost homes are:
But though older far

Than oldest yew,—
As our hills are, old,—
Worn new
Again and again:
Young as our streams
After rain:
And as dear
As the earth which you prove
That we love.

Make me content
With some sweetness
From Wales
Whose nightingales
Have no wings,—
From Wiltshire and Kent
And Herefordshire,
And the villages there,—
From the names, and the things
No less.
Let me sometimes dance
With you,
Or climb
Or stand perchance
In ecstasy,
Fixed and free
In a rhyme,
As poets do.

Edward Thomas

from BURNT NORTON

Words move, music moves
Only in time; but that which is only living
Can only die. Words, after speech, reach
Into the silence. Only by the form, the pattern,
Can words or music reach
The stillness, as a Chinese jar still
Moves perpetually in its stillness.
Not the stillness of the violin, while the note lasts,
Not that only, but the co-existence,
Or say that the end precedes the beginning,
And the end and the beginning were always there
Before the beginning and after the end.
And all is always now. Words strain,
Crack and sometimes break, under the burden,
Under the tension, slip, slide, perish,
Decay with imprecision, will not stay in place,
Will not stay still.

T. S. Eliot

WINGED WORDS

As darting swallows skim across a pool,
  Whose tranquil depths reflect a tranquil sky,
So, o'er the depths of silence, dark and cool,
  Our winged words dart playfully,
    And seldom break
  The quiet surface of the lake,
    As they flit by.

Mary Coleridge

LITTLE GIRL, BE CAREFUL WHAT YOU SAY

Little girl, be careful what you say
when you make talk with words, words —
for words are made of syllables
and syllables, child, are made of air —
and air is so thin — air is the breath of God —
air is finer than fire or mist,
finer than water or moonlight,
finer than spiderwebs in the moon,
finer than water-flowers in the morning:
   and words are strong, too,
   stronger than rocks or steel
stronger than potatoes, corn, fish, cattle,
and soft, too, soft as little pigeon-eggs,
soft as the music of humming bird wings.
   So, little girl, when you speak greetings,
when you tell jokes, make wishes or prayers,
   be careful, be careless, be careful,
   be what you wish to be.

Carl Sandburg

TALK

I wish people, when you sit near them,
wouldn't think it necessary to make conversation
and send thin draughts of words
blowing down your neck and your ears
and giving you a cold in your inside.

D. H. Lawrence

A CLASS-ROOM

The day was wide and that whole room was wide,
The sun slanting across the desks, the dust
Of chalk rising. I was listening
As if for the first time,
As if I'd never heard our tongue before,
As if a music came alive for me.
And so it did upon the lift of language,
A battle poem, *Lepanto*. In my blood
The high call stirred and brimmed.
I was possessed yet coming for the first
Time into my own
Country of green and sunlight,
Place of harvest and waiting
Where the corn would never all be garnered but
Leave in the sun always at least one swathe.
So from a battle I learnt this healing peace,
Language a spell over the hungry dreams,
A password and a key. That day is still
Locked in my mind. When poetry is spoken
That door is opened and the light is shed,
The gold of language tongued and minted fresh.
And later I began to use my words,
Stared into verse within that class-room and
Was called at last only by kind inquiry
'How old are you?' 'Thirteen'
'You are a thinker'. More than thought it was
That caught me up excited, charged and changed,
Made ready for the next fine spell of words,
Locked into language with a golden key.

Elizabeth Jennings

from A BOISTEROUS POEM ABOUT POETRY

I say this is a time for Poetry.
I name today the greatest of all days
That ever called a poet out to sing.
Not for its gentleness, for it has none:
Not for its colour or its love of song,
For it has none of either, as we know.
It is the empty clamour of its need,
Its wilderness of craving silences
That makes me call today a poet's day.
The themes! the themes! The unattempted songs!
The dictionaries crammed with eager ghosts!
Our hearts are ill with silence — someone must sing:
We have grown yellow on a diet of prose.

John Wain

POEM: A REMINDER

Capital letters prompting every line,
Lines printed down the centre of each page,
Clear spaces between groups of these, combine
In a convention of respectable age
To mean: 'Read carefully. Each word we chose
Has rhythm and sound and sense. This is not prose.'

Robert Graves

TO A POET A THOUSAND YEARS HENCE

I who am dead a thousand years,
    And wrote this sweet archaic song,
Send you my words for messengers
    The way I shall not pass along.

I care not if you bridge the seas,
    Or ride secure the cruel sky,
Or build consummate palaces
    Of metal or of masonry.

But have you wine and music still,
    And statues and a bright-eyed love,
And foolish thoughts of good and ill,
    And prayers to them who sit above?

How shall we conquer? Like a wind
    That falls at eve our fancies blow,
And old Mæonides the blind
    Said it three thousand years ago.

O friend unseen, unborn, unknown,
    Student of our sweet English tongue,
Read out my words at night, alone:
    I was a poet, I was young.

Since I can never see your face,
    And never shake you by the hand,
I send my soul through time and space
    To greet you. You will understand.

James Elroy Flecker

POETRY

When they say
That every day
Men die miserably without it:
I doubt it.

I have known several men and women
Replete with the stuff
Who died quite miserably
Enough.

And to hear of the human race's antennae!
Then I
Wonder what human race
They have in mind.
One of the poets I most admire
Is blind,
For instance. You wouldn't trust him
To lead you to the Gents:
Let alone through the future tense.

And unacknowledged legislators!
How's that for insane afflatus?
Not one I've met
Is the sort of bore
To wish to draft a law.

No,

I like what vamped me
In my youth:
Tune, argument,
Colour, truth.

Kit Wright

ONE POET VISITS ANOTHER

His car was worth a thousand pounds and more,
A tall and glossy black silk hat he wore;
His clothes were pressed, like pretty leaves, when they
Are found in Bibles closed for many a day;
Until the birds I love dropped something that —
   As white as milk, but thick as any cream —
Went pit, pit, pat! Right on his lovely hat!

Lead this unhappy poet to his car —
   Where is his longing now, where his desire?
When left alone, I'll ride him to his grave,
   On my own little horse of wind and fire.

W. H. Davies

When words we want, Love teacheth to endite;
And what we blush to speake, she bids us write.

Robert Herrick

MEMORABILIA.

I

Ah, did you once see Shelley plain,
   And did he stop and speak to you
And did you speak to him again?
   How strange it seems and new!

II

But you were living before that,
   And also you are living after;
And the memory I started at —
   My starting moves your laughter.

III

I crossed a moor, with a name of its own
   And a certain use in the world no doubt,
Yet a hand's-breadth of it shines alone
   'Mid the blank miles round about:

IV

For there I picked up on the heather
   And there I put inside my breast
A moulted feather, an eagle-feather!
   Well, I forget the rest.

Robert Browning

SHE WRITES HER FIRST POEM

Nothing remarkable. A lisp on paper.
Perfectly spelled; the scansion adequate
Provided you work out which words to lean on.

She keeps no record of the thing itself
But later may recall that it began
'Oh how I wish I had...' A knocking bet;
She is a calculating little girl.

Later she will not call to mind the words
Much less the subject. But the praise, the praise!
The tilted heads, moist eyes and steepled hands,
The implication that she had 'done well'.
And the reward; the gentle revelation
That being read is being listened-to.

This is her first taste of the subtle joy
Of writing down something she dare not say
So as to pass it, like a folded note,
From a safe place behind a grown-up's chair.

Her mother has it still, though God knows where.

Ann Drysdale

TO SCHOOL!

Let all the little poets be gathered together in classes
And let prizes be given to them by the Prize Asses
And let them be sure to call all the little poets young
And worse follow what's bad begun
But do not expect the Muse to attend this school
Why look already how far off she has flown, she is no fool.

Stevie Smith

FRANCIS

Today you told me how the wind
Frightened the washing and yesterday
When we sat down to picnic
In a shining field of hay
You said you could not eat because
You'd swallowed so much sun.
I scratch and grub to make from wind and hay
My ill-shaped cups to catch a little sun.
Perhaps I should put down my pen
And close my eyes and let you spill
Your careless poems in my lap.

Susan Hamlyn

WORDS

WORDS, dear companions! In my curtained cot
I cooed and twittered like a nesting bird;
And women spoke around me; but no word
Came to my baby lips—I knew you not.

Yet laughter did I know. I have not learned
To laugh more gaily since I first began.
The reasons of his mirth are born in man;
But man was born to laugh ere he discerned.

And tears I knew. Who taught me how to cry?
Was it my mother's heart that whispered me?
Tears have I wept since then that none could see,
Nor laughed, as then I laughed, ere they were dry.

Words, dear companions! As the spirit grew,
I loved you more and more with every hour.
I felt the sweep, the whirlwind of the power
HE gave to man, when man created you.

Words, dear companions! glittering, fair and brave!
Rapt in your rapture I was whirled along,
Strong in the faith of old, the might of song,
Struck through the silent portals of the grave.

Words, dear companions! Into you I drove
The dark dumb devil that besets the heart;
Nature in you rose to a heavenly art,
And wrought on earth an airy heaven of love.

Ah, when ye leave me, will there yet remain
The laughter and the weeping all untaught?
And will they, in the realm of perfect thought,
Teach me new words to sing of life again?

Mary Coleridge

LETTER TO A BOY AT SCHOOL

George and me
We'll sing to one another
Like two birds upon a tree.
And that has seldom happened
With a boy and his own Mother.
That George and me
Both write poetry
Shows there's a sympathy
More than in every family
Between George and me.
I first wrote poetry to please my Dad
Who wanted to write novels and was sad;
He never could write more than the first pages,
And then he wrote so slowly that it took him ages.
But I wrote easily
Although in poetry;
And when I was a girl at school,
When I learned grammar and was taught a rule
Or I was taught the meaning of a word such as inanimate,
I'd write a poem out upon my slate,
With all I knew of words and grammar to that date.
But when I wrote for my dear father,
I always used to worry rather
And think that for a girl it might be waste of time
To spend her life and love in making rhyme;
And I thought, maybe
I should be better knitting for my baby.
And now my dear and youngest son
Has brains enough to find my verses fun;
And so my head's no longer in a whirl
Wondering if I ought to write them, being born a girl.
And so I'll make,
For George's sake,
As soon as I have time,
The very finest thing I can in rhyme;
And everything I know

And dream and hope will go
Into this book,
Which will be a good pie,
Since I write better than I cook.
And George and me
Will sit and sing to one another
Like two birds upon a tree.
And in our pie
I'll not write 'George and I',
Though both are in the nominative case;
Our poetry will be a pleasant place,
Where grammar is most right when it is wrong,
In ways that sound well, in a song.

Anna Wickham

from AURORA LEIGH

       Books, books, books!
I had found the secret of a garret-room
Piled high with cases in my father's name,
Piled high, packed large, — where, creeping in and out
Among the giant fossils of my past,
Like some small nimble mouse between the ribs
Of a mastodon, I nibbled here and there
At this or that box, pulling through the gap,
In heats of terror, haste, victorious joy,
The first book first. And how I felt it beat
Under my pillow, in the morning's dark,
An hour before the sun would let me read!
My books!

Elizabeth Barrett Browning

MARTHA

'Once...once upon a time...'
  Over and over again,
Martha would tell us her stories,
  In the hazel glen.

Hers were those clear grey eyes
  You watch, and the story seems
Told by their beautifulness
  Tranquil as dreams.

She'd sit with her two slim hands
  Clasped round her bended knees;
While we on our elbows lolled,
  And stared at ease.

Her voice and her narrow chin,
  Her grave small lovely head,
Seemed half the meaning
  Of the words she said.

'Once...once upon a time...'
  Like a dream you dream in the night,
Fairies and gnomes stole out
  In the leaf-green light.

And her beauty far away
  Would fade, as her voice ran on,
Till hazel and summer sun
  And all were gone:

All fordone and forgot;
  And like clouds in the height of the sky,
Our hearts stood still in the hush
  Of an age gone by.

Walter de la Mare

THE HOUSE WAS QUIET
AND THE WORLD WAS CALM

The house was quiet and the world was calm.
The reader became the book; and summer night

Was like the conscious being of the book.
The house was quiet and the world was calm.

The words were spoken as if there was no book,
Except that the reader leaned above the page,

Wanted to lean, wanted much most to be
The scholar to whom his book is true, to whom

The summer night is like a perfection of thought.
The house was quiet because it had to be.

The quiet was part of the meaning, part of the mind:
The access of perfection to the page.

And the world was calm. The truth in a calm world,
In which there is no other meaning, itself

Is calm, itself is summer and night, itself
Is the reader leaning late and reading there.

Wallace Stevens

A BOOK

There is no frigate like a book
  To take us lands away,
Nor any coursers like a page
  Of prancing poetry.
This traverse may the poorest take
  Without oppress of toll;
How frugal is the chariot
  That bears a human soul!

Emily Dickinson

'O FOR A BOOKE'

O for a Booke and a shadie nooke,
  eyther in-a-doore or out;
With the grene leaves whispering overhede,
  or the Streete cryes all about.
Where I maie Reade all at my ease,
  both of the Newe and Olde;
For a jollie goode Booke whereon to looke,
  is better to me than Golde.

Anon

AFTER THE BOOK IS CLOSED

Whether it is the words
  or their meanings,
Or the sounds they make,
  or the way they echo one another;
Or simply the pictures
  they paint in the imagination,
Or the ideas they begin,
  or their rhythms...

Whether it is the words
  or their histories,
Their curious journeys
  from one language to the next;
Or simply the shapes they make
  in the mouth –
Tongue and lips moving,
  breath flowing...

Whether it is the words
  or the letters used
To spell them, the patterns
  they make on the page;
Or simply the way they call feelings
  into the open
Like a fox seen suddenly in a field
  from a hurrying train...

Whether it is the words
    or the spaces between –
The white silences
    among the dark print,
I do not know.
    But I know this: that a poem
Will sing in my mind
    long after the book is closed.

Gerard Benson

LATE SUMMER

OH it's late summer and spring a forgotten dream,
Yes, it's late summer and little flood in the stream
Late summer now no glint in the moon's gleam
Birds don't sing any more as they did that night
When every hour was a chalice for delight
Birds are feeding now with a busy flight

So there's only one thing to do, to pick from the bough
The fruit that was blossom then, and is solid now
The fruit that is on its way when the petals blow

And there's only one word to say — a quiet word,
A word we don't remember — you never heard —
Don't turn your head — it was only a leaf that stirred.

Margaret Cropper

10 · *Shades of childhood*

The sound of laughing children, screaming children, jeering children, thinned away to their suppers. The hammock was empty – oh no! the little girl's doll lolled in it, forgotten till somebody remembered it. But I knew it had always lolled there, and would loll there forever; and forever under the apple tree a spotted toy horse would stand, when the children now sitting at their suppers came out in their latter years to sit on a seat in the evening sun.

I knew – I know – that childhood is one of the states of eternity, and 'in that state we came we shall return.'

Eleanor Farjeon: THE HORN BOOK

Stop then, before we enter. Now you can hear the hobby-horse plainly, the squeak of its hinges as the front legs dip, the clap of the yellow stand on the floor when its back legs rise; for Stella is riding him furiously now, to the time of the backwards and forwards rattle of the mysterious marble which someone once put in at the hole by the saddle. You have been in the room once before, you know. But then it was dark. The curtains were drawn round the door and round the window, and a lamp was burning on the wall above the fire, and the hobby-horse stood in silence, munching the ghost of corn from an empty nosebag, stabled in the shadows, put by for the night.

Frank Kendon: THE SMALL YEARS

Once, after relating an incident of his childhood, *Walter de la Mare* looked back on that bygone day and remarked reflectively . . . 'I wonder where that little boy is now?'

IT WAS LONG AGO

I'll tell you, shall I, something I remember?
Something that still means a great deal to me.
It was long ago.

A dusty road in summer I remember,
A mountain, and an old house, and a tree
That stood, you know,

Behind the house. An old woman I remember
In a red shawl with a grey cat on her knee
Humming under a tree.

She seemed the oldest thing I can remember,
But then perhaps I was not more than three.
It was long ago.

I dragged on the dusty road, and I remember
How the old woman looked over the fence at me
And seemed to know

How it felt to be three, and called out, I remember
'Do you like bilberries and cream for tea?'
I went under the tree

And while she hummed, and the cat purred, I remember
How she filled a saucer with berries and cream for me
So long ago,

Such berries and such cream as I remember
I never had seen before, and never see
Today, you know.

And that is almost all I can remember,
The house, the mountain, the grey cat on her knee,
Her red shawl, and the tree,

And the taste of the berries, the feel of the sun I remember,
And the smell of everything that used to be
So long ago,

Till the heat on the road outside again I remember,
And how the long dusty road seemed to have for me
No end, you know.

That is the farthest thing I can remember.
It won't mean much to you. It does to me.
Then I grew up, you see.

Eleanor Farjeon

from A FAREWELL

Remember me and smile, as smiling too,
    I have remembered things that went their way –
    The dolls with which I grew too wise to play –
Or over-wise – and kissed, as children do,
And so dismissed them...

Charlotte Mew

HOW TO BE OLD

It is easy to be young. (Everybody is,
at first.) It is not easy
to be old. It takes time.
Youth is given; age is achieved.
One must work a magic to mix with time
in order to become old.

Youth is given. One must put it away
like a doll in a closet,
take it out and play with it only
on holidays. One must have many dresses
and dress the doll impeccably
(but not to show the doll, to keep it hidden).

It is necessary to adore the doll,
to remember it in the dark on the ordinary
days, and every day congratulate
one's ageing face in the mirror.

In time one will be very old.
In time, one's life will be accomplished.
And in time, in time, the doll –
like new, though ancient – will be found.

May Swenson

THE PLAYGROUND

Be it a weakness, it deserves some praise,
We love the play-place of our early days;
The scene is touching, and the heart is stone
That feels not at that sight, and feels at none.
The wall on which we tried our graving skill,
The very name we carved subsisting still;
The bench on which we sat while deep employ'd,
Though mangled, hack'd, and hew'd, not yet destroy'd;
The little ones unbutton'd, glowing hot,
Playing our games, and on the very spot;
As happy as we once, to kneel and draw
The chalky ring, and knuckle down at taw
To pitch the ball into the grounded hat,
Or drive it devious with a dexterous pat;
The pleasing spectacle at once excites
Such recollection of our own delights,
That, viewing it, we seem almost t' obtain
Our innocent sweet simple years again.

William Cowper

CHILDREN IN THE SQUARE

I play now with the thought of being a child
As children in the square below me play
Soldiers or emperors, play at being me.
Almost we reach each other and convey
Ourselves almost into the other's world.

Theirs is the large and the complete success
Since wholly built by them. But I because
I have been in the square indeed like them
Must build from facts, must take my present theme
Not from imagination but from time.
They make a future from suggestions, hints,
While I must reconstruct my innocence.

Children are still in the square and I am here:
It is not I but they who have the power
To offer back a childhood to share.
Passive I let them play at being me
And slip into their country by that way.

Elizabeth Jennings

EUSTACE AND EDITH
Or the old Rocking-horse

Poor rocking-horse! Eustace, and Edith too,
Mount living steeds: she leans her dainty whip
Across thy smooth-worn flank, and feels thee dip
Beneath the pressure, while she dons a shoe,
Or lifts a glove, and thinks 'My childhood's gone!'
While the young statesman, with high hopes possest,
Lays a light hand upon thy yielding crest,
And rocks thee vacantly and passes on.
Yet they both love thee — nor would either brook
Thine absence from this hall, tho' other aims
And interests have supplanted thy mute claims,
And thou must be content with casual look
From those, who sought thee once with earnest will,
And gallop'd thee with all their might and skill.

How often, when the Meet was at the hall,
Those babes took horse, and, in their joy and pride,
Drew half the coverts of the country side;
Sweet innocents! for little Spot was all
Their kennel; hapless Reynard never knew
How wide a field his enemies embraced,
How both in fact and fancy he was chased.
And what that staunch old rocking-horse could do!
Oh! give him kindly greeting, man and maid,
And pat him, as you pass, with friendly hands,
In that dim window where disused he stands,
While o'er him breaks the limewalk's flickering shade;
No provender, no mate, no groom, has he —
His stall and pasture is your memory.

Charles Tennyson Turner

THE HOBBY HORSE

The hobby horse lies forgotten in the attic;
The uncle who made the beautiful hobby horse is far away;
The boy who rode the horse, tugging the reins as the wild mane
    flowed in the wind, has grown up.
The uncle who carved the noble wooden head is far, far away.
The toy horse lies forsaken in the attic.

But listen!
Can you hear the distant thunder of hooves?

Gerard Benson

SONG

I had a bicycle called 'Splendid',
A cricket-bat called 'The Rajah',
Eight box-kites and Scots soldiers
With kilts and red guns.
I had an album of postmarks,
A Longfellow with pictures,
Corduroy trousers that creaked,
A pencil with three colours.

Where do old things go to?
Could a cricket-bat be thrown away?
Where do the years go to?

Arthur Waley

TEDDY

Of course I had a Teddy; most kids did.
But most kids didn't share that stupid name:
I knew I'd been baptized after my dad
And his. Eight English kings were called the same,

Something to live up to. Oh, but *Teddy*:
I did so loathe those soppy syllables!
All my life I'd be a cuddly kiddy,
One of this hard world's inconsolables.

I murdered Teddy, pulled out both his eyes,
Pulled off a leg, an arm, ripped out some fur.
Stout *Edward* I remained, all my schooldays;
Then, grown-up, it was *Ted* that I'd prefer.

I'm ageing now. I guess he's still up there,
In mother's loft, my doleful Teddy-Bear.

Ted Walker

WIND-UP

Gagged on silence, with a look
Of terror in its little eyes,
The clockwork bird has lost its song
And cannot find out what went wrong
However hard it tries.

Broken-hearted, half-way through
The triumph of a gorgeous trill —
The universe seemed filled with sound
Then something juddered, thumped, unwound
And suddenly stopped still.

What a shame. It worked last year.
A Christmas bird should always sing.
Indeed it should, but so life goes
With all our bright arpeggios
Dependent on a spring,

And there it looks down from its branch
With empty throat and beak ajar
While underneath the glittering tree
A child who might have once been me
Winds up his brand new car.

John Mole

THE DOLL HOUSE

After the children left it, after it stood
For a while in the attic,
Along with the badminton set, and the skis too good
To be given away, and the Peerless Automatic
Popcorn Machine that used to fly into rages,
And the Dr Dolittle books, and the hamsters' cages,
She brought it down once more
To a bedroom, empty now, on the second floor
And put the furniture in.
                            There was nothing much
That couldn't be used again with a bit of repair.
It was all there,
Perfect and little and inviolate.
So, with the delicate touch
A jeweller learns, she mended the rocking chair,
Meticulously laundered
The gossamer parlour curtains, dusted the grate,
Glued the glazed turkey to the flowered plate,
And polished the Lilliput writing desk.
                                 She squandered
One bold October day and half the night
Binding the carpets round with a ribbon border;
Till, to her grave delight
(With the kettle upon the stove, the mirror's face
Scoured, the formal sofa set in its place),
She saw the dwelling decorous and in order.

It was a good house. It had been artfully built
By an idle carpenter once, when the times were duller.
The windows opened and closed. The knocker was gilt.
And every room was painted a suitable colour
Or papered to scale
For the sake of the miniature Adam and Chippendale.

And there were proper hallways,
Closets, lights, and a staircase. (What had always

Pleased her most
Was the tiny, exact, mahogany newel post.)
And always, too, wryly she thought to herself,
Absently pinning
A drapery's pleat, smoothing a cupboard shelf —
Always, from the beginning,
This outcome had been clear. Ah! She had known
Since the first clapboard was fitted, first rafter hung
(Yet not till now had known that she had known),
This was no daughters' fortune but her own —
Something cautiously lent to the careless young
To dazzle their cronies with for a handful of years
Till the season came
When their toys diminished to programmes and souvenirs,
To tousled orchids, diaries well in arrears,
Anonymous snapshots stuck round a mirror frame,
Or letters locked away.
                              Now seed of the past
Had fearfully flowered. Wholly her gift at last,
Here was her private estate, a peculiar treasure
Cut to her fancy's measure.
Now there was none to trespass, no one to mock
The extravagance of her sewing or her spending
(The tablecloth stitched out of lace, the grandfather's clock,
Stately upon the landing,
With its hands eternally pointing to ten past five).

Now all would thrive.
Over this house, most tranquil and complete,
Where no storm ever beat,
Whose innocent stair
No messenger ever climbed on quickened feet
With tidings either of rapture or of despair,

She was sole mistress. Through the panes she was able
To peer at her world reduced to the size of dream
But pure and unaltering.
                        There stood the dinner table,
Invincibly agleam
With the undishevelled candles, the flowers that bloomed
Forever and forever,
The wine that never
Spilled on the cloth or sickened or was consumed.

The *Times* lay at the doorsill, but it told
Daily the same unstirring report. The fire
Painted upon the hearth would not turn cold,
Or the constant hour change, or the heart tire
Of what it must pursue,
Or the guest depart, or anything here be old.

'Nor ever,' she whispered, 'bid the spring adieu.'

And caught into this web of quietnesses
Where there was neither After nor Before,
She reached her hand to stroke the unwithering grasses
Beside the small and incorruptible door.

Phyllis McGinley

TO ANY READER

As from the house your mother sees
You playing round the garden trees,
So you may see, if you will look
Through the windows of this book,
Another child, far, far away,
And in another garden, play.
But do not think you can at all,
By knocking on the window, call
That child to hear you. He intent
Is all on his play-business bent.
He does not hear; he will not look,
Nor yet be lured out of this book.
For, long ago, the truth to say,
He has grown up and gone away,
And it is but a child of air
That lingers in the garden there.

Robert Louis Stevenson

from A SECOND CHILDHOOD

When all my days are ending
    And I have no song to sing,
I think I shall not be too old
    To stare at everything
As I stared once at a nursery door
    And a tall tree and a swing...

G. K. Chesterton

TO AN INFANT GRANDCHILD

Dear Katherine, your future
Can never meet my past.
So short our common frontier,
Our hinterlands so vast.

Yet at the customs post
Light airs pass freely over
And all we need to know
We know of one another.

Though day will wake your country
As dark flows over mine
Your outback sleeps in shadow now.
Your smile is cloudless dawn.

E. J. Scovell

WHO?

Who is that child I see wandering, wandering
Down by the side of the quivering stream?
Why does he seem not to hear, though I call to him?
Where does he come from, and what is his name?

Why do I see him at sunrise and sunset
Taking, in old-fashioned clothes, the same track?
Why, when he walks, does he cast not a shadow
Though the sun rises and falls at his back?

Why does the dust lie so thick on the hedgerow
By the great field where a horse pulls the plough?
Why do I see only meadows, where houses
Stand in a line by the riverside now?

Why does he move like a wraith by the water,
Soft as the thistledown on the breeze blown?
When I draw near him so that I may hear him,
Why does he say that his name is my own?

Charles Causley

from DREAMS OF A SUMMER NIGHT

The shades of childhood
Rise before me
Turning away their
Forgotten faces
But still I see
Like a glass of tears
The eyes of childhood
Gaze upon me.

Why do they turn
Away from me
Every wild one of
My shades of childhood?
Each seems to see
The ghost of its conscience
Like a white presence
Standing by me.

Then who tell me who
Ah who are they
The forgotten faces
Mopping and mowing
In Time like a tree?
Foretelling foreknowing
All the sad stories
That are now the memories
Of what had to be.

Is it I or you
O shades of childhood
I hear mourning in
Time like a tree?
O angel shades
Rise up and cover
Our eyes so that we
Cannot see.

Never no never
Ever return to
That wild wood
Where like larks
We once rose and sang
O shades of childhood
Crowd now around me
As here in my heart our
Shadows hang.

I hear them sighing
Like voices that fade
When the song is over
As shade after shade
Falls away from me:
O shades of childhood
Farewell for ever.
Remember me. O
Remember me!

George Barker

Acknowledgements

The Editor and Publishers are grateful to the following copyright holders for permission to include copyright material in this anthology:

Anna Adams: 'Roger Bavidge' © 1995, to the author. John Adlard: 'Cedar Tree' from *The Lichfield Elegies*, Aylesford Press 1991 ©1995 Rebecca Adlard. Joan Aiken: 'The Shadow on the Map' ©1960, to the author. W.H. Auden: ' If I Could Tell You' from *Collected Shorter Poems* 1968, to Faber & Faber Ltd. George Barker: 'For Shades of Childhood' from *Dreams of a Summer Night*, Faber 1968, to Faber & Faber Ltd. Frances Bellerby: 'Ends Meet' from *Selected Poems*, Enitharmon Press 1986, ©Charles Causley 1986, to David Higham Associates. Hilaire Belloc: 'The Early Morning' from *Collected Poems*, Duckworth 1970, to Peters, Fraser & Dunlop for The Estate of Hilaire Belloc. Gerard Benson: 'After the Book Is Closed' from *Evidence of Elephants*, Viking 1995, 'The Hobby Horse' from *The Magnificent Callisto*, Blackie 1992, Puffin 1994, to the author. James Berry: 'Isn't My Name Magical?' from *A Caribbean Dozen*, Walker Books ©1994, to the author. Wendell Berry: 'Song 4' from *Collected Poems 1957-1982*, ©1984 Wendell Berry, reprinted by permission of North Point Press, a division of Farrar, Strauss & Giroux Inc. John Betjeman: lines from 'Summoned by Bells', John Murray 1960, and 'East Anglian Bathe' from *Collected Poems*, John Murray 1958, to the publishers. Elizabeth Bewick: ' Catch a Snowflake' from *Heartsease*, Peterloo Poets 1991, to the author. Alison Bielski: for 'Dancing Class' from *Poetry Wales* and *For Today and Tomorrow*, ed. Howard Sergeant, Evans 1974, to the author. Guy Boas: 'The Curtain Falls' from *Selected Light Verse of G.B. of Punch*, The Shakespeare Head, 1964, to Punch. Jacqueline Brown: 'Getting It Wrong' ©1994, to the author. Alan Brownjohn: 'Seven Activities for a Young Child' and 'Marginalia' from *Collected Poems 1952-1983*, Secker and Warburg, to the author. Charles Causley: 'By St Thomas Water', 'Who?' and 'First Day' from *Collected Poems*, Macmillan 1992, to David Higham Associates. Leonard Clark: 'The Quilt', 'Let's Pretend' from *Collected Poems & Verses for Children*, Dennis Dobson 1975, to Robert Clark for the Literary Estate of Leonard Clark. Frances Cornford: 'The Grandson Dresses Up', 'Village before Sunset', 'Cornish Waking', 'The Conscript' and 'Summer Beach' from *Selected Poems*, ed. Jane Dowson, Enitharmon, 1996, to Dr. H. W. Cornford for the Literary Estate of Frances Cornford. Noel Coward: 'The Boy Actor' from *Not Yet the Dodo*, London & New York 1967, and *Collected Verse*, Methuen 1984, to Reed Books Ltd and the Estate of Noel Coward. E.E. Cummings: 'maggie and milly and molly and may' from *Complete Poems 1904-1962 of E.E. Cummings*, edited by George J. Firmage, ©1956/84/91, to W.W. Norton & Co.Ltd and the Trustees for the E.E. Cummings Estate. Neil Curry: 'The Doll's House' from *Ships in Bottles*, Enitharmon Press, ©1988, to the author. C.Day Lewis: 'Walking Away' and 'Learning to Talk' from *Collected Poems*, ©1992, Sinclair Stevenson, to the publisher. Jan Dean: 'Uniform' from *Nearly Thirteen*, Poetry Originals, ©1994 Blackie, to the author. Geoffrey Dearmer: 'Catherine's Story' from *A Pilgrim's Song*, ©1989, to the author. Walter de la Mare: 'The Shadow', 'The Bards', 'The Cupboard', 'And So To Bed',

'Martha', 'Ann, Upon the Stroke of Three' from *Complete Poems* ©1969, Faber, to the Literary Trustees of Walter de la Mare and The Society of Authors as their representative. Ann Drysdale: 'Tin Wheels', 'She Writes Her First Poem' from *The Turn of the Cucumber*, Peterloo Poets 1994, to the author. Helen Dunmore: 'Rag Doll' from *Secrets*, The Bodley Head 1994, to the author. T.S. Eliot: lines from 'Burnt Norton' from *Four Quartets*, 1935, to Faber and Faber Ltd. D.J. Enright: 'Two Bad Things at Infant School and Two Good Things', and 'Jephson Gardens' from *Collected Poems*, OUP, to the author, OUP and Watson Little Ltd. U.A. Fanthorpe: 'Half-Past Two' from *Neck Verse*, Peterloo Poets 1992, to the publishers. Eleanor Farjeon: 'It Was Long Ago', 'The Other Child', 'The Night Will Never Stay', 'The Tide In The River', and 'Seeking', to David Higham Associates & Gervase Farjeon for the Estate of Eleanor Farjeon. Michael Frayn: 'When I Was Your Age' from *All Sorts of Poems*, Angus & Robertson 1975, to the author and Greene & Heaton Ltd. Robert Frost: 'Revelation' and 'Acquainted with the Night' from *The Poetry of Robert Frost* edited Edward Connery Lathem, Jonathan Cape, ©1928, 1934, 1969, by Holt, Rinehart & Winston, ©1956, 1962, by Robert Frost, to the Estate of Robert Frost and Henry Holt & Co Inc. and The Random Century Group. Roy Fuller: 'In the Public Library' from *The World Through The Window*, Blackie 1989, ©John Fuller. Robert Graves: 'The Cool Web', 'The Corner Knot', 'The Penny Fiddle' from *Collected Poems*, Cassell 1975 and 'The Forbidden Play' from *The Penny Fiddle*, Cassell 1960, to Carcanet Press for the Robert Graves Estate. Susan Hamlyn: 'Francis' ©1995 to the author. David Harsent: 'The Rag Doll to the Heedless Child' and 'Owl' to the author. Seamus Heaney: 'Alphabets (1)' from *The Haw Lantern*, ©1981, 1987 to Faber & Faber Ltd. Diana Hendry: ' Dancing Class' from *Strange Goings On*, Poetry Originals, Viking 1995; ' Speaking Properly' from *Making Blue*, Peterloo Poets, 1995, to the author. Phoebe Hesketh: 'Paint-Box' from *Netting the Sun*, Enitharmon Press, 1989 to the author. Russell Hoban: 'Original Tin', ' Tin Frog', 'Katya Plays Haydn', ' Laura Round & Round' from *The Pedalling Man*, Heinemann 1969/1991 & Mammoth/Reed Books 1992, to the author. Ralph Hodgson: 'Time, You Old Gipsy Man' from *Poems 1917*, Macmillan, to Macmillan General Books & Macmillan Publishers Co. USA. Molly Holden: 'R Falling Out of Bed' from *Selected Poems*, Carcanet Press 1987 ©Alan Holden. Kenneth Hopkins: 'On Setting My Class Their First Quiz' from *Collected Poems*, Southern Illinois University Press 1964, to Laurence Pollinger Ltd for the Estate of Kenneth Hopkins. Langston Hughes: 'Poem' from *The Dream Keeper*, to Pluto Press. Ted Hughes: 'Full Moon and Little Frieda' from *Wodwo* ©1967, to Faber & Faber Ltd. Elizabeth Jennings: 'A Bird in the House', ' A Classroom', 'In the Night', 'The Child & The Shadow' from *Collected Poems*, Carcanet Press; 'Children in the Square' to David Higham Associates. Brian Jones: 'You Learning To Read' from *The Spitfire on the Northern Line*, Chatto & Windus 1975, to the author. Jackie Kay: 'Big Hole' from *Two's Company*, Blackie Poetry Originals 1992/Puffin 1994 to the author. John Latham: 'Dotting the 'i's' in Mississippi' from *The Other*

Side of the Street, Peterloo Poets 1985, to the author. Edward Lowbury: 'Nothing' from *Collected Poems*, Hippopotamus Press, to publisher and author. George Macbeth: 'A Child's Garden' from *The Broken Places*, Scorpion Press 1963, ©Penny Macbeth. Norman MacCaig: 'Aunt Julia' from *Collected Poems*, Chatto & Windus 1985, to the Random Century Group. Louis MacNeice: 'Intimations of Mortality' from *Collected Poems*, Faber & Faber 1966, to David Higham Associates for the Estate of Louis MacNeice. John Masefield: 'Sea Fever' from *Collected Poems*, Heinemann 1923, to the Society of Authors as the Literary executor of the Estate of John Masefield. Derwent May: 'A Midsummer Night's Dream in Regent's Park', to the author. Barry Maybury: 'Little Dolly Daydream' to the author. Phyllis McGinley: 'The Doll House' from *Three Times Three*, Secker & Warburg 1949, to Reed Books. Roger McGough: 'First Day At School' from *In the Classroom*, Cape, ©1976, 'Cinders' from *Defying Gravity*, Viking ©1992, to the author. Ian McMillan: 'Why We Need Libraries' from *Dad, The Donkey's on Fire*, Carcanet Press 1994, to the author. Edna St Vincent Millay: ' Look, Edwin! Do you see that boy' from 'A Very Little Sphinx' from *Collected Poems*, HarperCollins, ©1929, 1956 by Edna St Vincent Millay and Norma Millay Ellis, to Elizabeth Barnett, literary representative. A.A. Milne: 'Morning Walk' from *Now We Are Six*, Methuen 1927 to Reed Consumer Books. John Mole: 'Song of the Hat-Raising Doll' from *The Mad Parrot's Countdown*, 'The Smile' from *Boo to a Goose*, 'Wind-Up' from *Depending on the Light*, all Peterloo Poets ©John Mole 1987, 1990, 1995, to the author. Edwin Muir: 'The Child Dying' from *Collected Poems*, Faber 1951 and 1960, to the publisher. Ogden Nash: 'One Times One is Eight' from *Verses from 1992 On*, Little, Brown & Co. 1959, to Curtis Brown Ltd,. ©Ogden Nash, renewed. Norman Nicholson: 'Rising Five', 'To a Child Before Birth' from *Collected Poems*, Faber & Faber, ©Irvine Hunt 1994, to David Higham Associates. Dorothy Nimmo: 'Moggy at Grimma's' ©1995, to the author. Gareth Owen: 'Wedding Day' from *Song of the City*, Fontana Young Lions, an imprint of HarperCollins Publishers Ltd, to the author and publisher. Brian Patten: 'A Few Questions About Romeo' from *Love Poems*, George Allen & Unwin, ©Brian Patten 1981, 1984, to the author. Kathleen Raine: 'Spell of Creation' from *Collected Poems*, Hamish Hamilton 1981, 'The Eternal Child' from *Selected Poems*, Golgonooza 1988, to the author. Alastair Reid: 'The O-Filler', 'Play the Tune Again' from *Weathering*, Canongate Books Ltd 1987, to the publisher. James Reeves: 'The Black Pebble' from *The Blackbird in the Lilac*, OUP ©James Reeves 1952, to the James Reeves Estate. Theodore Roethke: 'The Waking' from *Collected Poems*, Faber 1968, to Faber & Faber and Doubleday, a Division of Bantam Doubleday Dell Publishing Group Inc. E. V. Rieu: 'Night Thoughts' from *The Flattered Flying Fish*, Methuen 1962, ©P. A. Rieu. Carl Sandburg: 'Little girl, Be Careful What You Say' from *The Complete Poems of Carl Sandburg*, ©1950 by Carl Sandburg and renewed 1978 by Margaret Sandburg, Helga Sandburg Crile and Janet Sandburg, to Harcourt Brace & Co. Siegfried Sassoon: 'The Child at the Window' from *Collected Poems*, Faber 1947, 1964, 1984, ©George T Sassoon. Carole Satyamurti: 'Broken Moon' from *Broken Moon*, 'Fatima' from *Striking Distances*, OUP.1987/1994 c, to the author. Vernon Scannell: 'Hide and Seek', 'View from a High-Chair', ' Words and Monsters' ©Vernon Scannell, to the author. E.J. Scovell: 'Protest', 'A Voice', 'Soloists', 'To an Infant Grandchild' from *Collected Poems*, Carcanet Press, ©the publisher. Ian Serraillier: 'Anne and the Field-Mouse' from *Happily Ever After*, OUP 1963, ©Anne Serraillier. Stevie Smith: 'Human Affection', 'Papa love Baby', 'To School' from *Collected Poems of Stevie Smith*, Penguin 1985, to James MacGibbon for the Literary Estate of Stevie Smith. Stephen Spender: ' My Parents' from *Collected Poems* 1928-1985, ©1985 to Faber & Faber Ltd. Wallace Stevens: 'The House was Quiet and the World Was Calm' from *Collected Poems of Wallace Stevens*, ©The Estate of Wallace Stevens, to Faber & Faber Ltd and Alfred A Knopf Inc. L.A.G. Strong: 'The Knowledgeable Child' from *Selected Poems*, Collins to Peters, Fraser & Dunlop Group. David Sutton: 'Hush-A-Bye-Baby' from *Settlements*, Peterloo Poets ©1991, to the author. May Swenson: 'How To Be Old' from *Nature: Poems Old & New by May Swenson* ©1994 The Literary Estate of May Swenson, to Houghton Mifflin Co. All rights reserved; originally published in The New Yorker. George Szirtes: 'A Small Girl Swinging' from *The Photographer in Winter*, Secker & Warburg, ©1986, to the author. A.S.J. Tessimond: 'Saving Grace', 'Dancing', from *Collected Poems*, Whiteknights Press, University of Reading ©1986 Dr Cedric Brown. Colin Thiele: 'Bird in the Classroom' from *Selected Poems*, Rigby 1970, ©the author. R.S. Thomas: 'Children's Song' from *Selected Poems*, 1946-1968, Bloodaxe Books, ©1986, the author. Anthony Thwaite: 'White Snow' from *The Owl in the Tree*, OUP 1963, 'Bournemouth 1939' from *In Time of War*, Penguin 1989 ©the author. John Wain: extract from 'A Boisterous Poem About Poetry' from *Weep before God*, Macmillan 1961 ©John Wain 1961, to Curtis Brown Ltd on behalf of the John Wain Estate. Ted Walker: 'Teddy' from *Grandad's Seagulls*, Poetry Originals, Blackie 1994, to the author and Sheil Land Associates. John Walsh: 'Evening in the Park' from *The Roundabout by the Sea*, OUP 1960, 'Shadows on Bantwick Sand', 'The Swing' from *Poets in Hand*, Puffin 1984, ©Mary Walsh. Anna Wickham: 'Letter to a Boy at School' from *The Writings of Anna Wickham*, Virago ©1984, James & George Hepburn. Richard Wilbur: 'Boy at the Window' from *Poems 1943-1956*, Faber & Faber Ltd. Kit Wright: 'Poetry' from *Short Afternoons*, Hutchinson ©Kit Wright 1989, to the author. Andrew Young: 'A Dead Bird' from *Collected Poems*, Secker & Warburg 1985 ©Alison Young on behalf of the Andrew Young Estate.

The Editor and Publishers thank the following for kind permission to use prose extracts: Christobel Burniston, Christopher Fry and the OUP; Sir John Gielgud; Elizabeth Jennings; Katrina Hendry for the Estate of Eiluned Lewis; Frederick Muller and Gregory & Radice for the Estate of Eve Garnett; A.P.Watt Ltd on behalf of the Trustees of the Robert Graves Copyright Trust; John Johnson Ltd on behalf of the literary executor of Forrest Reid.

Index of Poets

Anna Adams   b. 1926   136
John Adlard   1929-1993   144
Joan Aiken   b.1924   145
W.H. Auden   1907-1973   106

George Barker   1913-1991   240
William Barnes   1801-1886   129
Frances Bellerby   1899-1975   172
Hilaire Belloc   1870-1953   99
Gerard Benson   b.1931   221,231
James Berry   b.1924   113
Wendell Berry   b.1934   176
John Betjeman   1906-1984   43,135,159
Elizabeth Bewick   b.1919 20
Alison Bielski   b.1925   181
Laurence Binyon   1869-1945   180
William Blake   1757-1827   5,88
Guy Boas   1896-1966   193
Rupert Brooke   1887-1915   162
Jacqueline Brown   b.1944   188
Elizabeth Barrett Browning   1806-1861   217
Robert Browning   1812-1889   212
Alan Brownjohn   b.1931   32,140
Christobel Burniston   b.1909   201

Charles Causley   b.1917   115,168,239
G.K. Chesterton   1874-1936   237
John Clare   1793-1864   73,110
Leonard Clark   1905-1981   78,167
Mary Coleridge   1861-1907   107,205,215
Samuel Taylor Coleridge   1772-1834   41
Susan Coolidge   1835-1905   81
Frances Cornford   1886-1960   77,88,155,157,161
Noel Coward   1899-1973   190
William Cowper   1731-1800   228
Margaret Cropper   1886-1980   222
E.E. Cummings   1894-1962   158
Neil Curry   b.1937   34

Samuel Daniel   1563-1619   87
W.H. Davies   1871-1940   211
C. Day Lewis   1904-1972   16, 117
Walter de la Mare   1873-1956   11,23,47,
64,95,218,223
Jan Dean   b.1950   127
Geoffrey Dearmer   1893-1995   146
Charles Dickens   1812-1870   153
Emily Dickinson   1830-1886   132,162,220
Ann Drysdale   b.1946   45,213
Helen Dunmore   b.1952   35

George Eliot   1819-1880   70
T.S. Eliot   1886-1965   205
D.J. Enright   b.1920   80, 119

U.A. Fanthorpe   b.1929   118
Eleanor Farjeon   1881-1965   49,68,94,
98,155,223, 225
Rachel Field   1894-1942   194
Edward Fitzgerald   1809-1883   197
James Elroy Flecker   1884-1915   209
Marjory Fleming   1803-1811   25
Michael Frayn   b.1933   53
Robert Frost   1874-1963   74,164
Christopher Fry   b.1907   101
Roy Fuller   1912-1991   149

Eve Garnett   1900-1991   101
John Gielgud   b.1904   177
Rumer Godden   b.1907   29
Robert Graves   1895-1985   1,184,192,203,208
Dora Greenwell   1821-1882   89

Carolyn Hall   91
Susan Hamlyn   b.1953   214
Thomas Hardy   1840-1928   39
David Harsent   b.1942   33,165
Elizabeth Anne Hart   1822-1888   72
Seamus Heaney   b.1939   111
Diana Hendry   b.1941   173,182
Helen Henschel   Early 20thC   185
Robert Herrick   1591-1674   97,170,211
Phoebe Hesketh   b.1909   116
Russell Hoban   b.1925   44,50,187
Ralph Hodgson   1871-1962   105
Molly Holden   1927-1981   92
Thomas Hood   1799-1845   4
Gerard Manley Hopkins   1844-1889   100
Kenneth Hopkins   1914-1988   142
A.E. Housman   1859-1936   199
Barbara Howes   90
Langston Hughes   1902-1967   129
Ted Hughes   b.1930   125

Jean Ingelow   1820-1897   37, 51

Elizabeth Jennings b.1926   46,65,97,201,207,229
Brian Jones   b.1938   120
Ben Jonson   1572-1637   87

Jackie Kay   b.1961   130
John Keats   1795-1821   74,98

Frank Kendon   1893-1959   223
Charles Kingsley   1819-1875   38

John Latham   b.1937   134
D.H. Lawrence   1885-1930   187,206
Anne Lewis   b.1933   189
Eiluned Lewis   1900-1979   57
H.W. Longfellow   1807-1882   57
Edward Lowbury   b.1913   93

George Macbeth   1932-1992   26
Norman MacCaig   1910-1996   174
Louis MacNeice   1910-l963   96
John Masefield   1878-1967   156
Derwent May   b.1930   198
Barry Maybury   b.1931   76
Phyllis McGinley   1905-1978   234
Roger McGough   b.1937   112,196
Ian McMillan   b.1957   148
Charlotte Mew   1870-1928   179,226
Edna St Vincent Millay   1892-1950   60
A.A. Milne   1882-1956   56
John Mole   b.l941   36,131,233
Merrill Moore   b.1903   75
Thomas More   1478-1535   31
Edwin Muir   1887-1959   171

Ogden Nash   1902-1971   14
Norman Nicholson   1914-1987   6,62
Dorothy Nimmo   b.1932   24

Seamus O'Sullivan   1879-1958   179
Gareth Owen   b.1936   79

Coventry Patmore   1823-1896   42
Brian Patten   b.1946   139
Anna M.Pratt   114

Kathleen Raine   b.1908   3,7
James Reeves   1909-1978   157
Alastair Reid   b.1926   150,186
Forrest Reid   1875-1947   81
E.V. Rieu   1887-1972   89
Elizabeth Maddox Roberts   1886-1941   128
Theodore Roethke   1908-1963   99
Christina Rossetti   1830-1894   36,104,107,
                             122, 133,156,163,170
John Ruskin   1819-1900   29

Carl Sandburg   1878-1967   206
Siegfried Sassoon   1886-1967   27

Carole Satyamurti   b.l939   126,141
Vernon Scannell   b.1922   13,69,121
E.J. Scovell   b.1907   9,17,183,238
Ian Serraillier   1912-1994   48
William Shakespeare   1564-1616 63,137,195,197
Percy Bysshe Shelley   1792-1822   175
Jane Shore   138
John Skelton   c1460-1529   8
Menella Bute Smedley   1820-1877   72
Stevie Smith   1902-1971   15,21,80,214
Stephen Spender   1909-1995   128
Wallace Stevens   1878-1955   219
Robert Louis Stevenson   1850-1894   40,50,
                                        63,95,237
L.A.G. Strong   1896-1958   166
David Sutton   b.1944   12
May Swenson   1927-1989   227
Algernon Charles Swinburne   1837-1909   52
Sir Philip Sydney   1554-1586   61
George Szirtes   b.1948   86

Ann Taylor   1782-1866   14
Jane Taylor   1783-1824   14
Alfred, Lord Tennyson   1809-1892   109
Ellen Terry   1847-1928   177
A.S.J. Tessimond   1902-1962   132,183
Colin Thiele   b.1920   143
Edward Thomas   1878-1917   17,103,123,204
R.S. Thomas   b.1913   28
D'Arcy Wentworth Thompson   1829-1902   158
Francis Thompson   1859-1907   18
Anthony Thwaite   b.1930   19,161
Thomas Traherne   1637-1674   l,10,66
Charles Tennyson Turner   1808-1879   230
Elizabeth Turner   1775-1846   22

John Wain   1925-l994   208
Arthur Waley   1889-1966   231
Ted Walker   b.1934   232
John Walsh   19ll-1972   83,85,160
Anna Wickham   1884-1947   217
Richard Wilbur   b.1929   61
Humbert Wolfe   1885-1940   59
William Wordsworth   1770-1850   75,108, 203
Kit Wright   b.1944   210

Charlotte Yonge   1823-1966   153
Andrew Young   1885-1971   45

Index of Titles and First Lines

A cool small evening
  shrunk to a dog bark 125
A little child 7
A millionbillionwillion
  miles from home 112
A piper in the streets today 179
A sea-bird's shadow went
  across the wall 157
A shadow his father makes
  with joined hands 111
Acquainted with the Night 164
After the Book is Closed 221
After the children left it,
  after it stood 234
After the pantomime,
  carrying you back to the car 196
Ah cease thy Tears and Sobs,
  my little Life 41
Ah, did you once see Shelley
  -plain 212
Ah, that was but the wind 45
All right, dear, I'll not risk
  bad dreams again 12
All round the house is the
  jet-black night 95
All the bells of heaven
  may ring 52
All the bells were ringing 36
Alphabets 111
And So To Bed 95
And what if Romeo 139
And what will they
  remember when 198
Ann, Upon the Stroke
  of Three 47
Ann, upon the stroke of three 47
Anne and the Field-Mouse 48
Anthony 138
Apostate 81
Are they shadows that we see? 87
As darting swallows skim
  across a pool 205
As from the house your
  mother sees 237
As I was sitting, late
  last night 165
As Joe was at play 22
At the Theatre 194
Auguries of Innocence from 5
Aunt Julia 174
Aunt Julia spoke Gaelic 174
Aurora Leigh from 217
Autobiography 153

Baby, my dolly, oh, she
  never cries 35
Bards, The 11
Be it a weakness, it
  deserves some praise 228
Big Hole 130

Bird in the Classroom 143
Bird in the House, A 46
Bird's Eye View, A 72
Black Pebble, The 157
Boisterous Poem About
  Poetry, A from 208
Book, A 220
Books, books, books 217
Bournemouth,
  September 3rd, 1939 161
Boy Actor, The 190
Boy at the Window 61
Boy in the Dusk 59
Broken Doll, The 36
Broken Moon 126
Brother and Sister Sonnets 70
Burnt Norton from 205
But borne, and like a short
  Delight 170
By Saint Mary, my lady 8
By St Thomas Water 168
By St Thomas Water 168

Call out. Call loud: 'I'm ready!
  Come and find me!' 69
Can you find me? 101
Capital letters prompting
  every line 208
Catch a snowflake if you can 20
Catch a Snowflake If
  You Can 20
Catherine's Story 146
Centuries of Meditation 1
Cedar Tree 144
Child and the Shadow, The 65
Child and the Shell, The 75
Child at the Window, The 27
Child Dying, The 171
Child in the Orchard, The 103
Child upon the Stair, A 91
Childhood 31
Childhood from 110
Childhood of Edward
  Thomas, The 123
Children are dumb to say
  how hot the day is 203
Children in the Square 229
Child's Garden, A 26
Child's Laughter, A 52
Children's Hour, The 57
Children's Song 28
Cinders 196
Class, this is Fatima 141
Class-Room, A 207
Come, my darling, come away 14
Conscript, The 161
Consulting Summer's
  Clock 162
Consulting summer's clock 162
Cool Web, The 203

Corner Knot, The 184
Cornish Waking 157
Cupboard, The 23
Curtain, The 193

Dance to your daddie 181
Dancing Class 181
Dancing Class 182
Darling little Cousin 122
David Copperfield 153
Dead Bird, The 45
Dear Katherine, your future 238
Dew on the Grass 57
Do not expect your child
  to be a genius 181
Doll House, The 234
Dolls, The 39
Doll's House, The 29
Doll's House, The 34
Don't turn round,
  Miss Fisher 134
Dotting the i's in
  Mississippi 134
Dreams of a Summer
  Night from 240
Dumb Soldier, The 40

Early Morning, The 99
Early Supper 90
East Anglian Bathe 159
Either old magic or new math 14
Ends Meet 172
Eternal Child, The 7
Eustace and Edith 230
Evening in the Park 83
Every night and every morn 5
Ex Libris 151

False Friends - Like 129
Farewell, A from 226
Fatima 141
Few Questions about
  Romeo, A 139
Fifty-three faces, sad and
  apprehensive 142
Firefly in the pool of water 128
Firefly Song 128
First Affections 101
First Day 115
First Day at School 112
Fish do not smile: their
  faces are not 132
Fo fum and look at the
  plunge in Grimma's Arden 24
Follow a shadow, it still
  flies you 87
For how long known this
  boundless wash of light 155
For in and out, above, below 197

Forbidden Play, The 192
Fragment of an English
  Opera 199
Francis 214
*From you have I been
  absent in the spring* 137
Full Moon and Little
  Frieda 125

*Gagged on silence, with a
  look* 233
George and me 216
Getting It Wrong 188
God's Grandeur 100
Going to Bed 89
Goodbye to All That 1
Grandson dresses up, The 77
*Granny and I with dear
  Dadu* 158
Great A, little a, bouncing B 111

Half-past Two 118
Hat, The 80
He and She 133
*He rolls in the orchard:
  he is stained with moss* 103
*He tried to tell them
  what he felt* 116
Her mother's out today 76
*Her sixth midsummer
  eve keeps Ruth awake* 93
Here thump on tray 13
Here we are all, by day 97
*Here we go round the
  mulberry bush* 13
Here We Go Round the
  Mulberry Bush 94
Hey, nonny no 180
Hickory Dickory Dock 48
Hide and Seek 69
*His car was worth a
  thousand pounds and more* 211
Hobby Horse, The 231
Horn Book,The 223
House Was Quiet and the
  World Was Calm, The 219
*How do I know? Why,
  one afternoon* 145
*How do you like to go up
  in a swing* 50
How Many? 104
*How many seconds in a
  minute?* 104
*How often, when the Meet
  was at the hall* 230
How to Be Old 227
Human Affection 15
*Hush-a-bye,baby, your
  milk's in the tin* 13
Hush-a-bye, Baby 12

I always see.-I don't know why 166
*I am the eldest. I arrogate
  roles round here* 188
I am called Childhood, in

play is all my mind 31
*I can remember. I can
  remember* 190
*I cannot choose but think
  upon the time* 70
*I flung my satchel out of
  the window* 146
*I had a bicycle called
  'Splendid',* 231
*I had a dove and the sweet
  dove died* 74
*I have a little shadow that
  goes in and out with me* 63
I have been a Naughty Girl 25
*I have been one acquainted
  with the night* 164
I have seen 75
*I have hopped, when properly
  wound up, the whole length* 44
I know a little cupboard 23
*I love my beautiful hat
  more than anything* 80
I love you with my linen heart 33
I loved my friend 129
*I must go down to the seas
  again,* 156
*I once had a sweet little
  doll, dears* 38
*I play now with the
  thought of being a child* 229
I raise my hat 36
I remember, I remember 4
I Remember, I Remember 4
I say this is a time for Poetry 208
*I studied my tables over
  and over* 114
*I think they were about
  as high* 179
*I wake to sleep, and take
  my waking slow* 99
*I was a child and
  overwhelmed: Mozart* 184
*I who am dead a thousand
  years* 209
I will make a small statue 59
*I wish people, when you
  sit near them* 206
If I Could Tell You 106
If we shadows have offended 197
*I'll tell you, shall I,
  something I remember?* 225
*I'll tell you the truth, Father,
  though your heart bleed* 192
'I'm rising five,' he said 62
In Praise of Isabel Pennell 8
*In summer months when
  he was four* 161
In the gloom of whiteness 17
In the Night 97
In the public library 149
In unexperienced Infancy 66
Intimations of Mortality 96
Isn't my Name Magical? 113
It began with a whisper 131
It is easy to be young.

(Everybody is 227
*It is eighteen years ago,
  almost to the day* 117
It is the mid-sixties, and it 148
'It is time to go to bed?' 89
*It was a yellow voice, a high,
  shrill treble in the nursery* 46
It was Long Ago 225

*James painted black
  moustaches round his nose* 77
*"Jane Searle, her book"
  the scrap of paper says* 151
Jephson Gardens 80

Katya Plays Haydn 187
Katya's fingers on the keys 187
Knowledgeable Child, The 166
Late Summer 222
Laughter of children brings 90
Laura Round and Round 50
Law and Justice 37
*Learning bad grammar,
  then getting blamed for it* 119
Learning to Go Alone 14
Learning to Talk 16
*Let all the little poets be
  gathered together in classes* 214
Let's have some poetry 201
Let's Pretend 78
Letter to a Boy at School 216
Life in a Liberty Bodice 201
*Light filtered through
  the cedar* 144
*Lillian McEever is bride
  for the day* 79
Little Dancers, The 180
Little Dolly Daydream 76
*Little Girl, be careful
  what you say* 206
*Little girl, be careful what
  you say* 206
Little Maiden, better tarry 79
Little Mistake, A 114
*Lonely, save for a few
  faint stars, the sky* 180
Look Edwin! 60
*Look Edwin! Do you see
  that boy?* 60
Lost Doll, The 38

Macbeth *from* 195
*maggie and milly and
  molly and may* 158
Marginalia 140
Martha 218
*Matthew, Mark, Luke
  and John* 91
Memorabilia 212
Midsummer-Night's
  Dream, A, *from* 197
Midsummer's Night's
  Dream in Regent's Park, A 198
Moggy at Grimma's 24
Moon Penny 125

Moon penny 125
Morning Walk, The 56
Mother I love you so 15
My aged friend, Miss
    Wilkinson 11
My best friend Jenny
    Colquhoun has moved on 130
My grandmother came down
    the steps into the garden 172
My little Son, who look'd
    from thoughtful eyes 42
My mother was a
    romantic girl 21
My Parents 128
My parents kept me from
    children who were rough 128
My Shadow 63
My summer ends, and
    term begins next week 161
Myope, jackdaw-tongued, I
    was fetched to school 115

'Night-night, my Precious!';
    Sweet dreams, Sweet!' 95
Night Thought 89
Night Will Never Stay, The 98
Nobody can see my name
    on me 113
Noise that Time makes, The 75
Not for his curly mop 136
Nothing 93
Nothing remarkable. A lisp
    on paper 213
Now this is Mary Queen
    of Scots 37
Now we're all going to
    try again, aren't we girls? 182
Now when I stand upon
    the stair alone 91
Nursery Rhyme 13
Nurse's Song 88

O-Filler, The 150
'O for a Booke' 220
O for a Booke and a
    shadie nooke 220
O Peggy Purey-Cust, how
    pure you were 135
O soft embalmer of the still
    midnight! 98
Ode, on the Intimations
    of Immortality from 108
Of course I had a Teddy;
    most kids did 232
Of Perfect Friendship 133
Oh, it's late summer and
    spring a forgotten dream 222
Oh, what's the good of
    staying up and yawning 89
Oh when the early morning
    at the seaside 159
On setting my class their
    first quizz 142
'Once...once upon a time...' 218

Once upon a schooltime 118
One noon in the library - I
    watched a man 150
One Poet Visits Another 211
One Times One is Eight 14
Open the doors 34
Original Tin 44
Other Child, The 49
Out of my window late at
    night I gape 97
Out of us all 204
Owl 165

Paint Box 116
Papa Love Baby 21
Piano 187
Piper, A 179
Play the tune again; but
    this time 186
Playground, The 228
Poem 129
Poem: A Reminder 208
Poetry 210
Poor rocking-horse!
    Eustace, and Edith too 230
Praeterita 29
Prelude, The from 203
Protest, A 9
The Purloiner 22

Quilt, The 167
Quoth the boy, "I'll climb
    that tree 72

R. Falling out of Bed 92
Rag Doll to the Heedless
    Child, The 33
Remember me and smile,
    as smiling too 226
Remember this, when
    childhood's far away 27
Retire, my daughter 199
Revelation 74
Rising Five 62
Rock-a-bye baby 11
Roger Bavidge 136
Rubaiyat of Omar
    Khayam, The from 197
Russian Doll 35

Safe were those evenings
    of the pre-war world 43
Salutation, The from 10
Saving Grace 132
Sea Fever 156
Seaside 162
Second Childhood, A from 237
See this small one, tiptoe on 16
Seeing the snowman
    standing all alone 61
Seeking 68
Seven Things to Do 32
Seven Times One 51
Shade Catchers, The 179

Shadow, The 64
Shadow on the Map, The 145
Shadow March 95
Shadows 87
Shadows in the Water 66
Shadows on Bantwick Sand 160
She Writes Her First Poem 213
Should one of us remember 133
Sir Edward Elgar 185
Small Girl Swinging, A 86
Smile, The 131
Small Yews, The 223
Snow 17
Softly in the dusk, a woman
    is singing to me 187
Soloists 183
Some there be that shadows kiss 63
Something this foggy day 163
Something this foggy day, a
    something which 163
Song 74
Song 109
Song 170
Song 231
Song (4) 176
Song of the Hat-Raising Doll 36
Sonnet 98 137
Sounds 107
Speak when ye're spoken tae 21
Speaking Properly 173
Spell of Creation 3
Stage Fright 189
Still morning 160
Story of My Life, The 177
Straight to the seesaw we
    both run 83
Summer Beach 155
Summoned by Bells from 43,135
Swiftly out from the
    friendly lilt of the band 162
Swing, The 50
Swing, The 85

Talk 206
Teddy 232
That day we said goodbye
    to her 167
That's how fooling often
    ends, you see 92
The audience is good.
    A lucky sign 189
The awaited moment, the
    ballerina parts 183
The babe is at peace within
    the womb 175
The child is slow to speak
    in words 17
The clock! 107
The day was wide and
    that whole room was wide 207
The garden swing at the
    lawn's edge 85

The bobby horse lies

forgotten in the attic	231	To Sleep	98	cartwheels, long legs flashing	50
The house was quiet and the world was calm	219	Today you told me how the wind	214	When little girls begin to walk	15
The infant while his mother peers at novels	149	To-morrow, and to-morrow, and to-morrow	195	When little Jane lifts up her head	68
The moon on the one hand, the dawn on the other	99	Toys, The	42	When Mozart was a tiny boy	185
The night will never stay	98	Tread Softly	152	When the curtain goes down at the end of the play	193
The noise that Time makes in passing by	75	Tread softly here, as ye would tread	152	When the grass was closely mown	40
The past it is a magic word	110	True friendship unfeigned	133	When the voices of children are heard on the green	88
The shades of childhood	240	Try to imagine, if you can	185	When the last of gloaming's gone	64
The shadows of the bannisters march march	96	Turn on the tap for straight and silver water in the sink	32	When they say	210
The sky is tin, the street is tin and	44	Twelve, small as six	126	When words we want, Love teacheth to endite	211
The students drowsed and drowned	143	Twice five years	203	'Whenever you dress me dolls, mammy'	39
The sun was bright when we went in	194	Two Bad Things in Infant School	119	Whether it is the words	221
The tide in the river	155	Two small children in the Gardens on Sunday	80	White Snow	19
The world is charged with the grandeur of God	100	Uniform	127	'White snow,' my daughter says, and sees	19
There can be no going back now	173	Unfriendly, friendly universe	171	Who?	239
There is a bush that no one sees	94	Upon a Child	170	Who can say	109
There is a moment country children know	88	Very Odd Fish, A	158	Who has seen the wind?	107
There is no frigate like a book	220	View from a High Chair	13	Who has seen the wind?	107
There was a time when meadow, grove, and stream	108	Village before Sunset	88	Who is that child I see wandering, wandering	239
There went three children down to the shore	157	Voice, A	17	Who was here. Before his cat	26
There's no dew left on the daisies and clover	51	W.A.Mozart	185	Why should we fear that which we cannot fly?	61
These little limbs	10	Waking, The	99	Why we need libraries	148
They might not need me - yet they might	132	Walking Away	117	Wind-Up	233
They were the very first of my found things	45	Wedding Day	79	Winged Words	205
This summer is your perfect summer	6	Weeks and weeks of	120	Within a thick and spreading hawthorn bush	73
Thrush's Nest, The	73	We found a mouse in the chalk quarry today	48	Within the circles of our lives	176
Tide in the River, The	155	We live in our own world	28	Within the flower there lies a seed	3
Time, You Old Gipsy Man	105	We make ourselves a place apart	74	Words	204
Time, you old gipsy man	105	What are Heavy?	156	Words	215
Time will say nothing but I told you so	106	What are heavy? Sea-sand and sorrow	156	Words and Monsters	121
Tin Frog, The	44	What heart could have thought you?	18	Words, dear companions! In my curtained cot	215
Tin Wheels	45	What Katy did	81	Words move, music moves	205
To a Child at the Piano	186	When all my days are ending	237		
To a Child Before Birth	6	When Anne and I go out a walk	56		
To a Poet a Thousand Years Hence	209	When first they pushed me	86	You Learning to Read	120
To a Snowflake	18	When he was eight years old he had become	121	"You'll grow," she said and that was that	127
To an Infant	41	When I am dead, my dearest	170	You shall be the father	78
To an Infant Grandchild	238	When I am hungry I must cry	9	Your absent name at rollcall was more present	138
To any Reader	237	When I held you up to my cheek you were cold	35	Your hands have rituals as old as springtime	183
To Lalla, reading my verses topsy turvy	122	When I put her in the swing	49	Your shadow I have seen you play with often	65
To my Niece, A.M.	15	When I was still a boy and mother's pride	129		
To School!	214	When I Was Your Age	53		
		When I was your age, child	53		
		When it was Munich, I was eight	140		
		When Laura turns five			